G000123735

AIR-TO-GROUND OPERATIONS

Brassey's Air Power: Aircraft,
Weapons Systems and Technology Series,

VOLUME 2

Brassey's Air Power:

Aircraft, Weapons Systems and Technology Series

General Editor: AIR VICE MARSHAL R. A. MASON, CBE, MA, RAF

This new series, consisting of eleven volumes, is aimed at the international officer cadet or junior officer level and is appropriate to the student, young professional and interested amateur who seek a sound basic knowledge of the technology of air forces. Each volume, written by an acknowledged expert, identifies the responsibilities and technical requirements of its subject and illustrates it with British, American, Russian, major European and Third World examples drawn from recent history and current events. The series is similar in approach and presentation to the highly successful Brassey's Battlefield Weapons Systems and Technology Series, and each volume, excluding the first, has self-test questions.

Volume 1. Air Power: An Overview of Roles
Air Vice Marshal R. A. Mason, CBE, MA, RAF

Volume 2. Air-to-Ground Operations
Air Vice Marshal J. R. Walker, CBE, AFC, RAF

Titles of Related Interest

J. GODDEN
Harrier: Ski Jump to Victory

P. G. HARRISON *et al.*
Military Helicopters

R. A. MASON
War in the Third Dimension: Essays in Contemporary Air Power

B. MYLES
Jump Jet, 2nd edition

K. PERKINS
Weapons and Warfare: Conventional Weapons and their Roles in Battle

AIR-TO-GROUND OPERATIONS

Air Vice Marshal J. R. Walker CBE, AFC, RAF

BRASSEY'S DEFENCE PUBLISHERS
(a member of the Pergamon Group)

LONDON · OXFORD · WASHINGTON · NEW YORK
BEIJING · FRANKFURT · SÃO PAULO · SYDNEY · TOKYO · TORONTO

U.K. (Editorial)	Brassey's Defence Publishers, 24 Gray's Inn Road, London WC1X 8HR
(Orders)	Brassey's Defence Publishers, Headington Hill Hall, Oxford OX3 0BW, England
U.S.A. (Editorial)	Pergamon-Brassey's International Defense Publishers, 1340 Old Chain Bridge Road, McLean, Virginia 22101, U.S.A.
(Orders)	Pergamon Press, Maxwell House, Fairview Park, Elmsford, New York 10523, U.S.A.
PEOPLE'S REPUBLIC OF CHINA	Pergamon Press, Qianmen Hotel, Beijing, People's Republic of China
FEDERAL REPUBLIC OF GERMANY	Pergamon Press, Hammerweg 6, D-6242 Kronberg, Federal Republic of Germany
BRAZIL	Pergamon Editora, Rua Eça de Queiros, 346, CEP 04011, São Paulo, Brazil
AUSTRALIA	Pergamon-Brassey's Defence Publishers, P.O. Box 544, Potts Point, N.S.W. 3011, Australia
JAPAN	Pergamon Press, 8th Floor, Matsuoka Central Building, 1–7–1 Nishishinjuku, Shinjuku-ku, Tokyo 160, Japan
CANADA	Pergamon Press Canada, Suite 104, 150 Consumers Road, Willowdale, Ontario M2J 1P9, Canada

First edition 1987

Library of Congress Cataloging in Publication Data

Walker, J.R.
Air-to-ground operations.
(Brassey's air power; v. 2)
Includes index.
1. Close air support. 2. Attack planes. 3. Fighter planes. I. Title.
II. Series.
UG700.W35 1986 358.4'142 86-23270

British Library Cataloguing in Publication Data

Walker, J.R.
Air-to-ground operations.—(Air power; v. 2)
1. Air warfare
I. Title II. Series
358.4'14 UG630

ISBN 0-08-033612-4 (Hardcover)
ISBN 0-08-033613-2 (Flexicover)

Printed in Great Britain by
Hazell Watson & Viney Limited,
Member of the BPCC Group,
Aylesbury, Bucks

Preface

A disappointment to a professional military man in this country must be the low level of debate about defence in general and tactical doctrine in particular. This is surprising for a number of reasons; the United Kingdom is justifiably proud of its heritage of parliamentary democracy which is based on the power of debate and reason; currently the two well-established political parties are divided fundamentally on a number of major defence issues, including the form and nature of the national deterrent force; the threat to Western norms and standards has never been so openly, and it must be admitted, honestly, outlined by those who follow the Communist line; and if this was not enough, the nation spends some £18 billion per year on defence, equivalent to about 15 pence on income tax, enough in sum, it would have been thought, to concentrate the mind.

But a more dynamic debate is found elsewhere. In the Federal Republic of Germany, where a certain geographical incentive is not hard to find; in the United States, where the freedom of information act has done much to provide the necessary raw material to allow debate and where the congressional committee system is a model of accountability to the taxpayer; but also, strangely, in that supposedly closed and secretive society the Soviet Union, where bookshops stock shelves with the cut and thrust of military debate ranging from nuclear deterrence through the gamut to infantry tactics. It is with some regret that it is necessary to confess to having more of the translated works of Soviet generals on the shelves of my own modest library than I have works of my fellow British generals, not through any partiality, merely through availability. If a military man is so poorly served, what of the interested civilian?

It is for the 'interested civilian' that this volume is primarily written; it may also hopefully act as a primer for the junior officer starting out on his career, but it is not aimed directly at the qualified warrior nor at those expert scientists, technicians and engineers who work so well, for so little praise, in our defence-related industries. Their fare needs to be of greater weight than this. Nor can this volume be a comprehensive catalogue of the air-to-ground operational art within the size constraints set upon me. Within those constraints, an attempt has been made to deal with some major areas at least enough to spark interest, perhaps enough to encourage greater enquiry, or even questioning, or better still disagreement leading to debate, rather than merely mentioning the great many factors which make up a successful fighter-bomber operation.

The majority of the material here bears upon the fighter-bomber. Following the demise of the Vulcan bomber, and the assumption by the Royal Navy of the national strategic deterrent role in the guise of the Polaris force, the Royal Air

Force has become increasingly a tactical, rather than a strategic, air force. In the last chapter it is suggested that there may be ways to reverse that trend and again assume the strategic reach, the need for which the early prophets such as Trenchard preached so convincingly. But meanwhile, the fighter-bomber provides the backbone of the offensive capability of the Royal Air Force. Writing part of a series on air operations gives the author of the air-to-ground volume a problem; the tool is the fighter-bomber, and the aircraft are well named—they are bombers because they carry bombs and their modern equivalents, but equally they are fighters and have in many cases the capability of fighters, operate using the same techniques as fighters and, most importantly, operate against fighters in penetrating to their targets. It is inevitable, therefore, that any work on fighter-bombing should overlap to some extent on that about the fighter role.

Air operations in general present a fascinating subject for study and life is rarely dull; in no other military field is technology moving so swiftly and forcing such changes in doctrine and attitude. In no other field do the practitioners train on a day-to-day basis so close to the operational case or pay such a penalty for error or inefficiency. No matter what the speciality, hunting submarines, rescuing those in distress, intercepting inquisitive Soviets, transporting freight or passengers on 'the world's safest airline', or offensive operations in the fighter-bombers, most crews will argue that theirs is the supreme test of the airman's art. And who is to disagree? Here no comparison is made; enough to say that the noble art of 'mud moving' is known to its devotees, reasonably, modestly and understandably, as the *Sport of Kings.*

Contents

List of Figures

List of Plates

1

Environment

The opening verses of the first chapter of the Bible tells how God created the world; he created the earth and light on the first day; vapour and water on the second; land, sea and plant life on the third; the sun, moon and stars on the fourth; and animal life on the fifth. It was only after the environment and nature had been organised did God create man, on his sixth, and last, working day. Genesis thereby contains a cautionary tale for man who, despite his many and great achievements, remains an afterthought; a prisoner of his environment. He may build shelter to protect him from winter, but he cannot prevent its onset; he may use ingenuity to see in the dark, but still it gets dark; he may forecast the wind, but cannot control the patterns which give rise to it.

The airman is one of a small group of the species *homo sapiens* to whom the physical effects of weather and environment assume a great, and on occasion overwhelming, importance. Together they can determine whether or not he can practice his art, for he is, more than most, a man of his medium. To be effective an airman has to understand his environment; he has to exploit the opportunities it offers and he ignores its pitfalls at his peril. The accident files provide copious proof of the fate which befalls those who go into the air without understanding the natural forces.

As in many fields, knowledge of the environment is increasing at an impressive pace. That this has occurred over the relatively short lifetime of aviation, a span within the memory of those still alive, is a tribute to the demands which aviation has made on the forecaster. Much progress has been made since the inquiry held into an early Royal Flying Corps accident concluded that the reason the aircraft had ended up embedded in the perimeter hedge was that the pilot had been taking off before sunrise and that 'it was clear that there was no lift in the air at such an early hour.' Then accidents occurred because the environment was not perfectly understood; now accidents occur despite our improved understanding of the environment, perhaps more so because of our imperfect understanding of the man. The man who flies without understanding his medium is a menace to himself and to those over whom he travels. Yet, as aviation extends its reach, now regularly and effectively, into those areas previously denied to it, all-weather operations and true night operations, there is more to learn. The scope is magnified further because it is not only the effect of environment on the human being which has to be appreciated, but also the effect on the variety of sensors which increasingly dominate the scene; radar, infrared devices, image intensifiers, all react in their own way to a variety of conditions and their characteristics have to be understood if a mission is to be executed successfully.

What are the dominant features of the environment? Visibility, cloud conditions, the occurrence of day and night, precipitation, wind direction and speed, temperature and irradiance. The list is not exhaustive and is in no order of priority, except that of man's own sensors his eyes are the most important, and the ability to see, governed mainly by visibility, is a case for this factor to be given precedence over the remainder. It is also implicit in some of the others; the unaided eye at night is an inefficient sensor and so reduces visibility, as does flight in cloud.

The scope of this volume does not allow the many environments world-wide to be mentioned separately, and uses mainly as examples the north-west European situation. In any case it would be unprofitable to attempt to be so comprehensive, because the purpose of using detail is not to produce a regional manual but to illustrate the *principles* which need to be considered. The detail will change according to the location; the principles, and way of looking at the problems, should hold good world-wide.

VISIBILITY

Visibility is a factor which can vary widely both within regions and between regions of the world. Aircrew can become accustomed to their particular region's characteristics and find it difficult, and sometimes traumatic, to change from one region to another. Aircrew attuned to the generally poor visibility in north-west Europe have become so confused by the unaccustomed visibility in the Southern United States that they have become 'temporarily unsure of their position'; some would even admit to being lost. When accustomed to the mists of the North German plain, the profusion of navigational features some fifty or more miles away can be an embarrassment. Equally, those pilots who train initially in the United States, such as those in the German Air Force, require a comprehensive orientation course on their return to Europe to accustom them to quite different operating conditions, a parallel to the experience during World War II when so many Allied aircrew were trained in the United States for operations in Europe. A practical concern leading from this centres on the effectiveness of the large numbers of reinforcement aircrew which are due into the European theatre from the United States in the event of a crisis. In circumstances where the opportunity to acclimatise to the changed conditions may not arise, their effectiveness may not be as high as peacetime evaluations indicate. An answer would be regular deployments to their likely operating areas, but cost, and the frequent necessity to counter rapid personnel rotation, argues against this as a complete answer. Although the example of US squadrons deploying into Europe is an easily understood environmental change, there are some weather factors which could provide similar problems for Warsaw Pact aircrew deploying from their rear areas to more forward locations.

In general, visibility in France is better than that in the Federal Republic of Germany (FRG); equally, it is better in East Germany and in Poland than in the FRG. The same general pattern exists from north to south, from North Cape to Sicily, where visibility on the flanks tends to be better than in the centre, although there are pockets in the south which suffer prolonged periods of poor visibility.

So much for generalities; it is when the discussion turns towards the specific that some care must be exercised. There are two problems: the first is that of the *collection* of statistics and the second is the *interpretation* of the statistics. 'Averages' have to be used with great care; an average for the FRG could include the predominantly flat North German Plain and the hilly areas of the south, the agricultural areas of north and south and the industrialised areas of the Ruhr, Hannover and Hamburg. There can be, and frequently are, major *micro* differences within the *macro* average. A further cause for care is that weather statistics indicate what *might* happen, not what necessarily *will* happen. Even further, there can be some difficulty in reconciling one set of statistics with another; each sound in their own right, but greatly varying in the basis for the assessment. Weather statistics should be looked upon, therefore, for overall patterns and trends, the general order of things, rather than for specifics.

For this reason it is always wise to suspect the interpretation placed upon the weather statistics until the basis of the figures quoted are understood. Particularly now that modern weapon systems are proliferating and many, in one way or another, are affected by weather conditions, there can be special pleading and highly selective use of weather data in support of one project over another. With such provisos in mind, what do the statistics show for visibility?

Figure 1.1 shows the mean value of visibility over the year for twenty-nine places in the FRG. In the lower visibility range of most interest to the ground attack pilot it can be seen that there is a visibility of less than 4 km for a quarter of the time and less than 8 km for half of the time. Converted to flying time at typical operational penetration speeds, this equates to only a little over 16 sec and 32 sec respectively; at typical attack speeds somewhat less.

Figure 1.2 shows the variation about the mean between summer and winter.

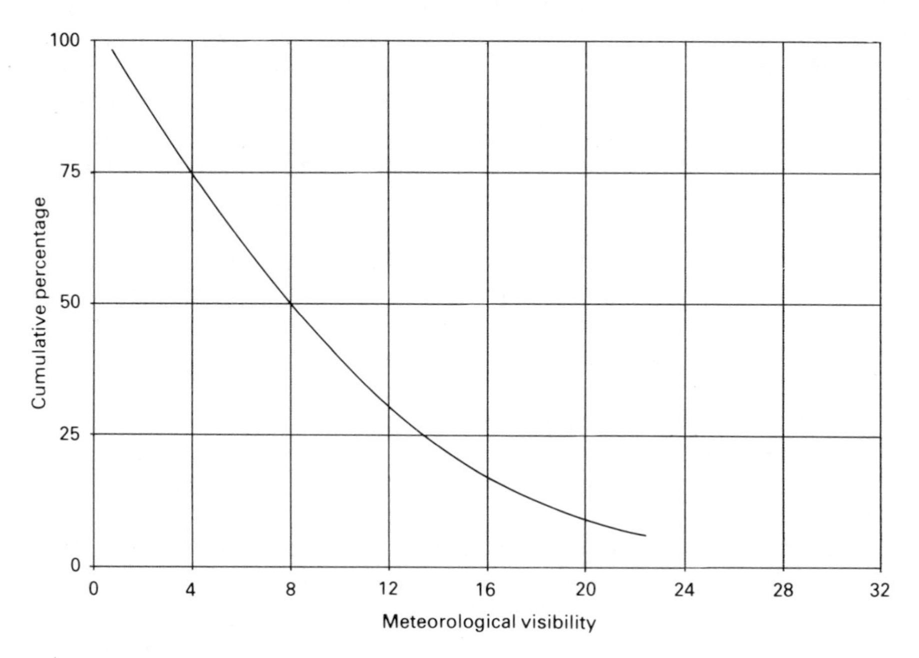

FIG. 1.1. Meteorological visibility (mean value over a year for twenty-nine places in the FRG).

While a visibility of 4 km or more will exist for 75 per cent of the time, on average it will vary between 87 per cent of the time in July and only 54 per cent of the time in December. The regional variations are indicated by the results of a French study which show that while the FRG may average 4 km or more for 75 per cent of the time, the variations within France range between 4 km or more for 81 per cent of the time of Dunkerque on the Channel coast to 98 per cent for those areas adjacent to the Mediterranean Sea.

Figure 1.3 shows the pattern regionally throughout the year, and from it the *macro* pattern of the visibility east to west and north to south can be derived. It is sobering to remember while studying these figures that at least one nation has spent considerable effort pursuing the design of a weapon which assumed a detection of the target from a range of 10 km, before eventually concluding that their philosophy was misguided. The example serves to remind that both the low and the mighty are vulnerable to ignorance of their medium.

Figure 1.4 shows the pattern in the FRG of the worst type of visibility condition, that of fog, varying from light fog to heavy fog. For practical purposes, this condition rules out a successful attack by a manned aircraft without considerable aid by a sophisticated weapon system. In most cases some form of automatic attack would be required. It can be seen that 9.4 per cent of the time some form of 'fog' condition exists, but the variation is important because it shows the high percentage of the time that 'fog' can exist in the winter months of December and January, 20 per cent and 17 per cent respectively.

CLOUD

Cloud to the ground-attack pilot is the ultimate zero visibility. Not only does it prevent him using his primary human sensor, the eyes, but can force him to use emitters such as radar or radio and so expose him to detection by a foe advanced enough to have the relevant equipment. Conversely, against a less advanced enemy, or even in tactical situations against quite advanced opposition, the use of cloud for concealment can be advantageous and can force an opponent to revert to a system rather than a visual attack. Even the short time needed for an opponent to change from one to the other can make a difference between delivering or receiving the first shot, or in escaping or being forced to fight, perhaps not normally on the best terms. Cloud is perhaps the greatest hindrance to formation operations, where the ability to see and be seen within the formation is fundamental to its mutual defence and important to its flight safety. It is practically very difficult, even in the most advanced of aircraft, to achieve the saturation of a target through a high concentration of aircraft over target if there is significant cloud about the operating levels in the vicinity of the target.

The more modern sensors become the norm, so the importance of the cloud conditions increase. Radar is mainly unaffected by cloud except in extreme circumstances, but image intensifiers and infrared devices can be rendered inoperative. Low cloud bases can therefore severely hamper operations which demand pull-up attacks, lengthy dives to lay weapons or to identify targets, or the delivery of weapons with electro-optical homing heads. It can also inhibit or impair certain complex fuzing systems.

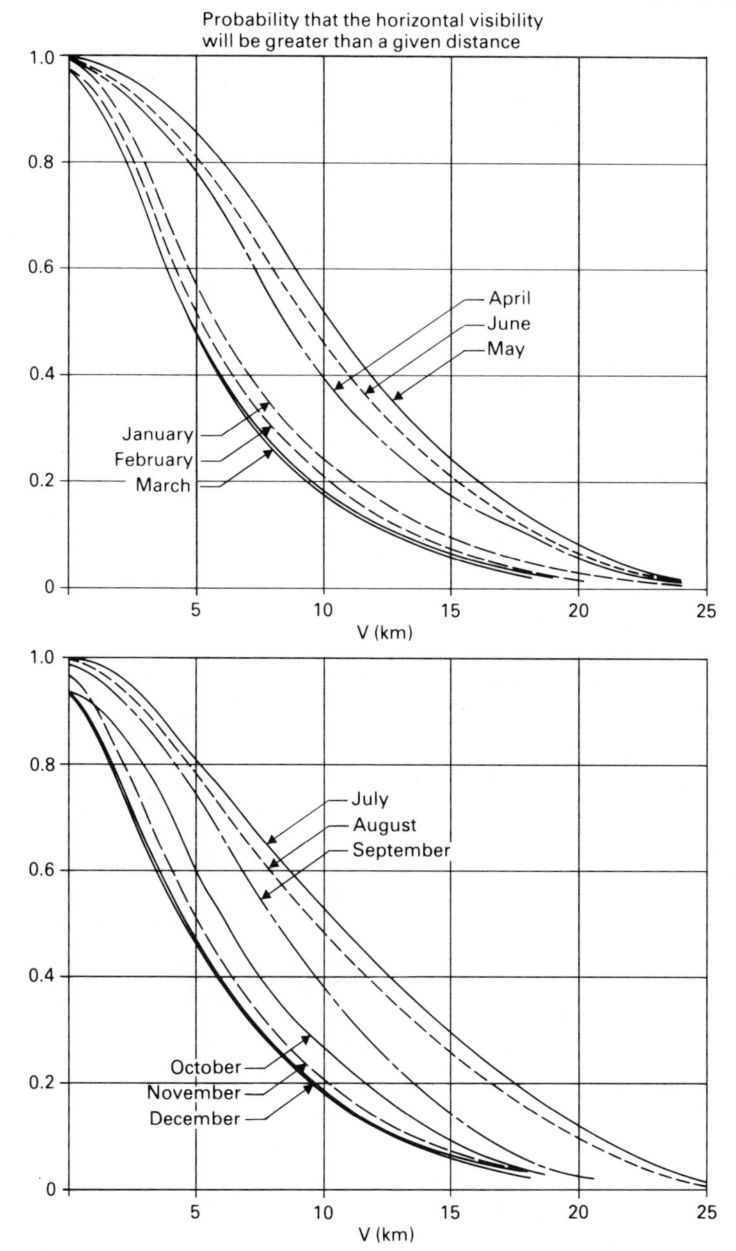

FIG. 1.2. Meteorological visibility.

Cloud cover varies regionally, by season, and throughout the 24-hour day. In Central Europe overcast (8/8ths) or nearly overcast (7/8ths) conditions occur about one-third of the time in summer and between a half to two-thirds of the time in winter, depending on location. Maximum cloud cover tends to occur in the early morning and is at a minimum during the day. The occurrence of fog, in effect

Central Europe	Visibility	Percentage of days in the month for which the visibility is											
		Jan.	Feb.	Mar.	Apr.	May.	June	July	Aug.	Sept.	Oct.	Nov.	Dec.
	Less than 10 km	70.7	67.8	60.9	44.5	34.1	33.5	37.3	40.5	55.4	66.2	74.3	74.1
Munster	Less than 4.8 km	46.1	41.5	33.7	13.7	13.5	12.7	17.6	20.2	24.0	41.4	46.2	50.5
	Less than 3.2 km	35.8	30.7	23.2	8.7	8.1	8.3	11.1	13.0	17.0	30.5	32.8	38.9
South Europe	Less than 10 km	98.8	99.1	97.7	97.3	97.1	95.2	96.1	96.9	99.2	99.2	99.7	99.5
Verona	Less than 5 km	96.8	96.7	89.9	89.7	67.3	65.8	63.0	67.7	79.8	89.7	94.7	97.1
Villafranca	Less than 3 km	90.2	86.0	85.3	51.2	38.9	30.0	21.8	36.8	49.2	70.0	81.2	91.0
	Less than 10 km	2.0	2.0	4.3	5.4	7.1	6.9	11.8	4.7	3.3	2.6	4.8	1.7
Trapani Burgi	Less than 5 km	0.2	0.8	1.2	1.1	1.5	0.7	2.4	0.4	0.1	0.4	1.0	0.1
(Sicily)	Less than 3 km	0.1	0.3	0.6	0.4	0.3	0.2	0.6	0.3	0.0	0.2	0.3	0.0
Italy	Less than 10 km	41	39	42	34	22	13	7	13	17	24	29	35
Tarante	Less than 4 km	6	5	5	6	3	1	0	1	2	3	4	4
Brindisi	Less than 10 km	37	31	20	23	11	7	7	8	23	19	21	37
	Less than 4 km	5	8	4	5	1	1	1	2	3	3	2	5

North Europe Norway	Visibility	Percentage of days in the month for which the visibility is											
		Jan.	Feb.	Mar.	Apr.	May.	June	July	Aug.	Sept.	Oct.	Nov.	Dec.
	Less than 10 km	16	15	15	11	3	2	2	4	6	10	10	12
Tromso	Less than 4 km	6	8	7	5	1	<1	0	1	1	2	3	4
Kantokaino	Less than 10 km	47	36	19	13	9	7	8	12	17	32	42	63
	Less than 4 km	20	15	9	8	5	2	2	5	7	17	19	24
Baltap	Less than 8 km	46	41	38	26	17	15	15	19	26	40	48	49
	Less than 5 km	34	30	27	16	10	8	9	11	18	24	34	35
	Less than 3 km	27	24	22	12	7	6	6	8	13	18	25	28
	Less than 8 km	28	30	33	21	12	6	6	9	14	20	22	25
	Less than 5 km	18	27	24	13	7	2	2	3	8	13	12	14
	Less than 3 km	14	22	21	10	5	1	1	2	5	9	8	10
Central Europe	Less than 10 km	69.7	65.6	64.2	45.5	30.8	22.3	28.9	35.7	50.3	64.5	73.5	72.3
Hamburg	Less than 4.8 km	45.6	49.1	37.6	14.9	10.0	10.9	11.3	15.1	20.3	38.2	52.8	53.8
	Less than 3.2 km	32.5	33.7	24.4	9.0	5.1	5.4	5.4	7.9	11.4	24.7	37.4	37.8

FIG. 1.3. Percentage of days in a month for which the visibility is less than a given distance.

cloud on the ground, varies between locations, but inland the tendency is towards a minimum during the day and a maximum during the night.

Figure 1.5 shows the average cloud cover for four contrasting regions of the FRG and shows what may be thought to be a surprising conformity throughout the year. But it is only cloud cover at the operating level which presents the ground-attack pilot with problems, and the figure shows a pattern of high cloud bases in summer and lower cloud bases in winter. This is of particular concern when training programmes and profiles are discussed. Although most aircrew will fly lower in war than they are allowed to by environmental pressures in peace, there are limits to how far training norms can be improved overnight, particularly when other pressures, fear and apprehension, will have their effect on performance.

Type of weather		J	F	M	A	M	J	J	A	S	O	N	D	Mean value %
Very fair weather	$V > 18$ km	3%	4	5	10	12	15	18	15	5	4	3	2	8
Fair weather	9 km $< V <$ 18 km	16%	19	22	33	38	40	40	39	39	28	20	19	29.4
Light haze	4 km $< V <$ 9 km	38%	38	40	41	37	34	29	30	37	37	36	34	36
Haze	1.8 km $< V <$ 4 km	26%	26	23	12	10	9	10	12	13	18	24	25	17.2
Light fog	0.9 km $< V <$ 0.9 km	8%	7	6	2	2	2	2	2	3	4	8	8	4.5
Fog	0.5 km $< V <$ 0.9 km	3%	2	2	1	1	0.5	1	1	1	2	3	3	1.7
Heavy fog	$V <$ 0.5 km	6%	4	2	1	0.5	0.5	0.5	1	2	7	6	9	3.2

FIG. 1.4. Meteorological visibility—fair weather, haze and fog.

Those air forces which train regularly at, say, 250 ft above ground level might reasonably expect the bulk of their crews to penetrate in war at heights around 150 ft. It might be less reasonable to expect aircrew from those air forces regularly training nearer 1,000 ft to approach these lower levels. As Fig. 1.6 shows, the aircrew constrained to 500 ft operationally will be able to operate on only 77 per cent of occasions in the winter, while those able to operate at 150 ft might be able to operate over 90 per cent of the time. In wars of high intensity and short duration, that 13 per cent difference could matter out of all proportion to its extent. More particularly, the figures refer to averages and in that period when the conditions lie below the average the case is even better made. Certainly the figures cannot be any comfort to those who would argue for any diminution of effective and realistic training at operationally viable levels.

Universal Time	0000	0300	0600	0900	1200	1500	1800	2100
Number of stations	15	14	22	22	22	22	20	15
January	6.0	6.2	6.3	6.6	6.4	6.4	6.1	6.0
February	5.8	5.9	6.4	6.3	6.2	6.0	5.8	5.5
March	4.7	4.8	5.7	5.6	5.5	5.4	5.2	4.5
April	4.2	4.6	5.2	5.5	5.6	5.6	5.2	4.3
May	4.0	4.8	5.2	5.2	5.5	5.4	5.1	4.5
June	4.2	5.1	5.1	5.1	5.5	5.4	5.0	4.7
July	4.0	4.9	5.1	5.3	5.4	5.3	5.0	4.7
August	3.8	4.5	5.3	5.2	5.4	5.2	5.0	4.3
September	4.0	4.3	5.3	5.2	5.2	5.1	4.8	4.0
October	4.6	4.9	5.9	5.8	5.5	5.3	4.9	4.6
November	5.9	5.6	6.5	6.7	6.6	6.4	6.0	6.0
December	6.3	6.4	6.6	6.8	6.7	6.6	6.2	6.2

FIG. 1.5. Average cloud cover in the FRG.

DAY AND NIGHT

As the sun travels inexorably up and down the latitudes of an earth spinning off-centre, so the length of day and night varies between the seasons. The higher, or lower, the latitude, so the effect is more marked to the extent that in the far north of Norway and Sweden a summer barbecue party in daylight after midnight is not an exceptional pastime. Conversely, the night, when it comes, can be long and unrelieved. Even in the more moderate latitudes about the fifties, covering the northern area of the Central Region, in winter it is effectively 'night' from the viewpoint of the ground-attack aircrew from about 1600 hr through to about 0800 hr; put another way, for two-thirds of the 'day' it is 'night'. Equally, in the summer the reverse is true and the concealment of night is limited to a few short hours.

Of all the environmental conditions, visibility, cloud, precipitation, etc., the day/night element is the most absolute. We know that the visibility *may* be poor, and we know the percentage *chance* of that happening, as we do with cloud or precipitation, but we *know* that it will become dark; we know it will become dark to a 100 per cent probability and to a high order of forecasting accuracy. Of the many imponderables, knowing when night will fall is not one of them; it is one of the great constants. What is of interest in view of this 'constant' is the effort which has been placed in the past into the more impressive 'all-weather' capability rather than in the less glamorous, but far more likely, night capability. Aircraft such as the F-111, introduced into service as early as 1968, and the Tornado, following twelve years later, have complex and expensive equipments to allow operations in

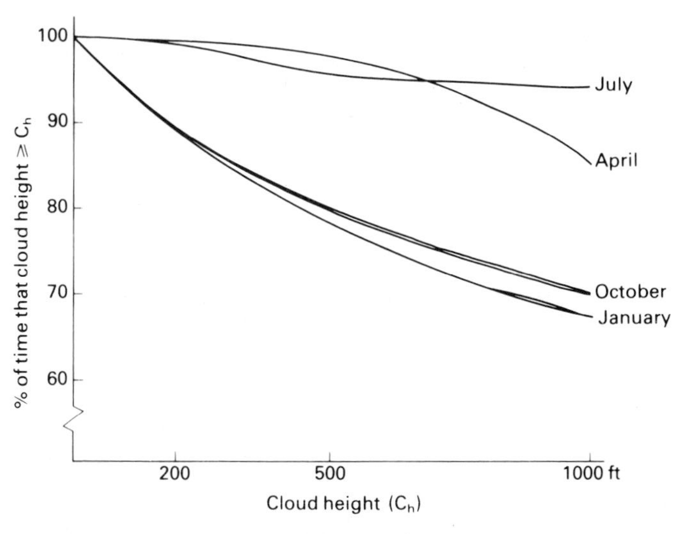

FIG. 1.6. Cloud height.

'all weather', while the vast bulk of NATO, and indeed Warsaw Pact, air power lack the ability to operate at night, even on fair weather nights. Yet relatively cheap night vision goggles can give a limited capability at night. Without this aid, an expensive force is impotent for as much as two-thirds of the 24-hr period in the winter. The cost-effectiveness argument for tackling night operations is indisputable. Even in the shortest war, a few days perhaps, it *will* get dark; it might not get "all weather'. This is not to say that all-weather capability should be ignored. On the contrary, the airman and designer must strive to rid air power of any artificial restrictions caused by environmental conditions. What is being discussed is the relative priorities, and they dictate that the 'sure' problem is addressed before the 'unsure' problem. For most air forces of the world, and debatably for all, effective night operations for the bulk of the force will have a greater return than a partial capability, at great cost, for a small proportion of the force.

'Day' and 'night' are convenient but simplistic terms. Too often discussion talks of 'day' and 'night' as if there are only two states, the light and the dark; conditions in which man can see, the day, and where he cannot see, the night. The real situation is far from this pure, and at the height of noon on a dull overcast day, perhaps flying alongside a tall dark cumulo-nimbus, the *effective* vision aircrew may have can be less than flying on a bright/moonlight night, down-moon, after a light rain shower when roads, canals, rivers, lakes and coastlines show in great clarity and cities, towns and villages are pools of shape-revealing light.

IRRADIANCE

The extreme level of 'irradiance' is bright sunlight and Fig. 1.7 gives a measure of the average 'insolation' of sixty French resorts over a period of 14 years.

While it could be expected that there was more sun in summer than winter, the measure of difference is notable; only one-fifth the sun in December than in the best month of July.

	J	F	M	A	M	J	J	A	S	O	N	D	Avg
Hours/month	75	100	175	200	225	225	250	225	175	150	75	50	192
%	10.5	14	24	28	31	31	35	31	24	21	10.5	7	22

FIG. 1.7. Average insolation for sixty French resorts.

As mentioned before, there is a wide variety of levels of irradiance; day and night cannot be looked upon in such pure terms as white and black, and an understanding of the high levels between the two extremes becomes important as more sensors rely upon light amplification in one sort or another for their effect. Figure 1.8 gives some indication of the graduation.

Condition	Irradiance (lux)
Noon, sunny, cloudless	100,000
Typical sunny day	10,000
Noon, cloudy	1,000
Sunrise or sunset	500
Very dark day	100
Full moon at zenith	0.2
Moonlight, various quarters no cloud	0.01 to 0.2
Night, no moon, stars	0.001
Night, no moon, cloudy	0.0003

FIG. 1.8. Natural irradiance.

PRECIPITATION

Precipitation is a vital part of nature's cycle of sun, land and sea and is usually remarkable only in its extreme. A skiing resort without snow is as unhappy as are the unirrigated places without rains when drought brings famine in its wake. Profusion of precipitation can paralyse the life of the most developed nations in winter, and floods can be devastating to property, crops, livestock and man. In either extreme form, scarcity or profusion, precipitation can represent nature in its most raw form.

To the airman, more than usually vulnerable to his medium, precipitation well within the extreme bounds can still cause problems. There are many aircraft in the inventories of the world, the front windscreens of which become opaque in even the lightest of drizzle. Curved quarter screens remain crystal clear, but the all-important front screen, made to high optical quality at great cost, is defeated by rain, so preventing the pilot placing his aiming index on the target. A whole mission can be frustrated by a light rain shower. Varying answers have been tried to control the problem. In the slower aircraft, windscreen wipers can be used, but airflows much above 300 kts make this an increasingly difficult engineering problem. Pastes and polishes exist and work in varying degrees of efficiency in trying to disperse the droplets. A very effective system is to use high-pressure air to blow the water clear of the screen, but this is costly in weight and complexity. Perhaps the best solution is the continuously curved windscreen, of which the F-16 mounts a good example, where a flat surface is absent and the droplets naturally disperse to the sides, but there are penalties to pay. It is difficult, and expensive, to achieve good optical quality in acrylics which have to be so contoured and made thick enough to withstand the very heavy shock loadings of birdstrike. Cockpit lighting reflections can also cause problems. Such difficulties might be thought to pale into insignificance compared to the possible alternative of being incapable of engaging the target, the *raison d'être* of a 'warplane'.

Snow can pose particular problems. Most airmen who have operated in northern climes, both aircrew and groundcrew, will be familiar with the difficulty of keeping airfields operational following, or during, snowstorms. A bone-numbing business at the best of times. If not conducted with great care and expertise, hard-packed ice ridges can be left on runways and taxiways and can remain until well into the balmy days of spring, playing havoc with both tyres and undercarriages of heavily-laden aircraft. As the thaw loosens the ice pack from the surface, it becomes a potent source of damage to engines, the equal of any stone. Over the years there has been much discussion about the best way to handle snow on an airfield. Some point to the success achieved by those used to snow, the Swedes and Norwegians for example, who believe in packing the snow deliberately and operating on top of it. It seems an attractive option, and in their particular circumstance it is, because once in place the snow can usually be relied upon to stay frozen until spring. Further south, however, a heavy snowfall followed by a slight thaw could give the problem of slush on the runway, arguably of more trouble than snow. A very few centimetres of slush can increase take-off runs excessively, even to the point of preventing take-off, and slush thrown into wheel wells and flap tracks, once frozen solid at high altitude, can prevent the operation of those services on return from the mission. Packed snow operation also demands concession in design. The Norwegian Air Force F-16, for example, has the special fitment of a braking parachute, unlike other F-16s; the Swedish Air Force's Viggen has a thrust reverser. Wheel braking cannot be relied upon, particularly as modern fighter design tends towards small and single-wheel undercarriage arrangements to save weight and space. This can give rise to braking problems which can prove to be a major operating limitation.

In the air, snow presents two main problems. The first is the phenomenon of 'white-out', familiar to Arctic explorers and an effect used in certain illusions relying on lack of contrast for their effect. It can be a most dangerous condition to the unwary. The combination of gently rolling terrain, undisturbed snow and low, bright, cloud on the hilltops has cost some dearly and caused many more to spend freely of adrenalin. Weapons, and more specifically sensors, know no fear, but they too can become confused. Snow cover affects the return from some radars, and snow-covered woods can give an erroneous indication of height under certain circumstances. Some scene-matching techniques could be affected by snow cover and give degraded results. In all, snow is not an airman's friend.

So how often does it occur? Again an area where a casual examination of the statistics can be confusing. Figures vary slightly with source, but in northern Germany there is snow in the month of January on only 0.9 per cent of occasions, or for about $6\frac{3}{4}$ hr. But unlike rain, snow does not drain away and a heavy fall over that period can be, and often is, enough to give major problems, particularly as snowfall tends to be cumulative in a prolonged cold spell. January's fall may add to December's and be reinforced by February's. Figure 1.9 shows the frequency of water forms in percentage terms for months indicative of the four seasons for northern Germany.

Month	Drizzle	Rain	Haze	Fog	Hail	Snow	No water
April	3.2	12.7	17.1	2.8	1.2	0	63
July	1.6	12.5	9.3	0.8	0	0	75.8
October	2.3	7.5	27.4	9.5	0	0	53.3
January	3.9	10.9	34.3	3.8	12.7	0.9	33.5

FIG. 1.9. Frequency of water forms in northern Germany.

Figure 1.10 shows the probability of rain precipitation heavier than certain intensities. In these statistics the rates of 1.5, 3 and 4.5 mm/hr have been used. There is some variation in the terms used to describe certain levels of precipitation, and while this can be a minor inconvenience to the expert it can be confusing and possibly hazardous to the airman. Many aviators will have descended into an airfield expecting a gentle drizzle to break out of cloud in what to him would best be described as a torrent. In fast jet operations the difference in perception between the meteorological observer and the pilot, and any difference in understood terminology, could materially affect decision-making and safety. A formation leader may be happy to penetrate the overcast and execute a formation landing if the precipitation is light, but may elect to split the formation into single aircraft units if the landing was to be made in heavy precipitation. Some modern aircraft can be skittish on runways with standing water, and a formation landing in such circumstances can be a potential double accident.

The UK *Forecasters Guide* offers the following advice: precipitation below 0.5 mm/hr is 'slight' and under such conditions 'puddles will form slowly, if at all'. Between 0.5 and 4 mm/hr water will be observed running freely down stand-pipes. Above 4 mm/hr the rain will give rise to a 'roaring noise' from roofs and will rebound to give a fine mist immediately above the ground.

	Intensity (mm/hr)		
	1.5	3	4.5
London	0.80	0.19	0.06
Paris	0.76	0.15	0.03
Berlin	0.76	0.15	0.03
Warsaw	0.76	0.15	0.03
Moscow	0.95	0.29	0.13
Average (%)	0.806	0.186	0.056
Hours/year	70.6	16.3	4.9

FIG. 1.10. Probability of rain precipitation heavier than certain intensities.

WIND VELOCITY

Wind *velocity* is a function of wind direction and wind speed. The two elements have different importance at different times in a mission. Generally concern about the wind velocity is concentrated about the take-off and landing phases of the flight; it is too often ignored when planning the conduct of the operational attack to the great disadvantage of achieving the object of the mission.

The arrangements of most airfields were determined after some research into the wind patterns for the locations concerned, and while most nations have the odd airfield where the research would seem to have been only cursory, most airfields have a runway which is more or less into wind for what turns out to be about two-thirds of the time. It is unprofitable to seek from the statistics justification for any general statement more definitive than this, because the effect of off-centreline wind varies greatly with the characteristics of the aircraft operating from it. One Western operational type has a cross-wind limitation as low as 15 kts; others can be safely operated above 30 kts. These are cross-wind *components*, not absolute wind speeds. Consequently, a wind as high as 60 kts blowing from 30° off a runway only gives a 30 kt component, but at these higher wind speeds the cross-wind component, despite its magnitude, can be the lesser of the evils, being normally accompanied by turbulence and wind-shear, the latter being particularly dangerous to larger aircraft.

Wind direction will also assume greater significance as operations tend to move progressively off-base. It hardly affects the vectored-thrust aircraft which can orientate into the prevailing wind for the final vertical part of the approach. But the Short Take-Off and Landing (STOL) aircraft making a conventional landing on a road strip with tree-lines close to the strip can find itself making the bulk of the approach under one wind condition of speed and direction only to find that as it approaches the critical touch-down point on a more restricted strip than normal, the shielding effect has materially altered the flight conditions. The more the conventional air forces become accustomed to the idea of operating off-base from these restricted strips, the more they need to take the attitude to turbulence and shear reflected in the naval airman's approach to wake, funnel and island effects on carriers.

Wind speed is normally the more important of the two components of wind velocity. With no speed, that is calm conditions, direction, even if it existed, would be irrelevant. Wind speed has important connotations on runway performance, shortening the ground roll of both take-off and landing. This factor could be of crucial importance when launching or recovering aircraft from damaged runways. In some parts of the world high wind speed can mean reduced visibility from dust and sand and can inhibit operations more than its modest dimension would suggest. Over the sea a high wind associated with a high sea state can give rise to fine mist held in suspension at the lower heights. Low flight at high speed under these conditions can result in salt-encrusted windscreens and partial obscuration of missile heads and electro-optical seekers. Similar effects can result from high-speed flight through a sand-laden lower atmosphere, except that whereas salt can be washed off, the scouring effect of high-speed sand impact can damage, or even ruin, delicate transparencies.

Too few aircrew apply the knowledge of the wind velocity to their tactical planning in the target area, but in many respects this is where it can most assist, or hinder, mission success. Attention tends to concentrate on the weapon-aiming aspects and this is quite proper, for an unguided weapon is influenced by the wind during its flight to the target and aim-off in excess of 50 ft is not uncommon in cross-winds of 30 kts. The turbulence normally associated with such speeds gives a difficult sight-handling problem at all but the shortest of ranges and overall weapons effects for forward-firing weapons will usually be degraded in high wind conditions. As forward-firing weapons tend to 'run with the line' of the attack, it is crosswind, more than head or tail winds, which causes the most trouble. Modern inertial weapon systems are programmed to allow for the wind effect, but it is important to understand their strengths and limitations. Velocity errors, which build up in the best of systems, can have a disproportionate effect on weapon-aiming solutions, but perhaps the greatest source of error is that the inertial system senses the wind velocity at the height at which the aircraft is flying. The bomb or shell will be affected by the wind velocity pertaining to the airspace between the release height and the ground, therefore, if the release height is high, or the target shielded in some way, or the conditions give strong wind-clear effects, the aiming system prediction will be in error. On some targets very small errors can result in total misses with not even collateral damage to the intended target.

Wind velocity can play an important part in the planning of an attack in the target area apart from the purely weapon-aiming aspects. An aircraft travels within the body of air which contains it, therefore the wind speed affects the aircraft's ground speed. As the vulnerability of an aircraft to ground defences is sensitive to the time it is exposed to them, the speed at which an attack can be flown can be important. By electing to attack downwind, and more than most the airman can select his attack direction, ground speed can be increased by the wind speed element. If planning is poorly conducted and the attack executed upwind, the difference between the two ground speeds will be twice the wind speed, a not inconsiderable factor if the wind is strong. This simple mathematics can be seen applied by the better display pilots at air shows where the slow-speed run will be demonstrated flying into wind to minimise the ground speed and the high-speed run flown downwind to maximise ground speed.

Figure 1.11 shows typical wind speed distribution for northern Germany. Figures for southern Germany are quite similar.

It is interesting to see that the popular perception of still summer days and cruel

Wind speed (kts)	Spring	Summer	Autumn	Winter
<6	26.7	28.1	26.8	25.2
7–10	29.9	30.1	26.3	28.3
11–16	21.9	19.8	18.1	20.8
$\leqslant 16$	78.5	78.0	71.2	74.3

FIG. 1.11. Percentage frequency of wind speed distribution.

winter winds is not necessarily borne out by the facts. To an approximation, about a quarter of the time there are winds over 16 kts regardless of season. It just feels stronger when it is cold!

TEMPERATURE

Aircraft able to operate world-wide have to be designed to a wide temperature tolerance and much time and trouble is expended to this end. The human being also has a wide temperature range to cope with, but is less susceptible to redesign or modification. Consequently, he must be operated with the temperature effects on his imperfect mechanisms appreciated and, where possible, mitigated by sensible education and the application of appropriate operational procedures. This is not a medical textbook, and comment will be restricted mainly to operational matters, but aircrew need to listen carefully to their medical officer on the subject of temperature effects and he should be a valued member of the planning team when deployments are made which span temperature zones.

Survival aspects tend to dominate discussion of temperature effects and perhaps understandably. Rather than being selfish or emotional, it makes good management sense to recover a downed pilot who in peace may cost £3 million to replace or in war could possess expertise difficult if not impossible to replace in the short time available.

Even in north-west Europe, a wide range of temperatures can be experienced; summer temperatures above 30°C and winter temperatures well below freezing. Yet school children are taught that the area lies in a *temperate* zone and perhaps this gives rise to some misconceptions. In summer, flying in bulky flying equipment, dehydration can be a problem, and the habit of always having a long drink before flying has merit. The problem becomes more acute as, increasingly, the question of continuing operations in Nuclear, Chemical or Biological (NBC) conditions looms larger. NBC suits are bulky, constricting and hot, not helped by the need to wear respirators or having to decontaminate to enter clean areas even to take liquid. The aircrew NBC suits, necessarily more complex because of the aircraft interface, are even more of a problem. Dehydration and heat exhaustion can be a major problem and one which can cause lower sortie rates from scarce aircrew. In merely posing the NBC threat, one side can reduce the other's capability.

Geography is also important when the capability of aircraft is considered. In some parts of the world it is possible to take off from a base in sweltering conditions wearing light summer flying equipment with little additional insulation underneath, when within a relatively few minutes an ejection could result in the aircrew facing a near-Arctic survival situation. The proximity of the US air bases in Arizona, Nevada and California to the Sierra Nevada range springs to mind, but the situation in South-West Asia with the Himalayas and the Hindu Kush is similar.

In winter, the ambient temperature may not be the killer, but the *chill factor* can transform the situation. Figure 1.12 shows how a wind can turn a bearable temperature into an effectively much lower temperature and the degree of effective reduction is impressive; so impressive, that it is sometimes not appreciated, or believed, until experienced in survival training—then it is rarely forgotten.

Wind speed (kts)	Ambient temperature (°C)				
	+4	+2	0	−2	−4
8	−2	−4	−7	−9	−11
12	−5	−8	−10	−13	−16
16	−7	−10	−13	−16	−19
19	−9	−12	−15	−18	−21
23	−11	−14	−17	−20	−23
27	−12	−15	−18	−21	−24
31	−12	−16	−19	−22	−25

FIG. 1.12. Equivalent chill temperature.

The temperature effect in water can result in very reduced survival times unless the correct equipment is available and used to its full capability. Some two-thirds of the earth is covered by water, and some airmen, the maritime patrol squadrons, for example, spend much of their flying lives over it, but the attack pilot must not discount the water. Landing in even European lakes in winter with a broken arm is a 'sea'-survival situation, and at least one pilot ejecting over the middle of Germany only just made it to the bank of the River Weser into which he inconveniently fell. Figure 1.13 shows graphically how life expectancy for the unprepared can be most adversely affected.

It is too easy to be mesmerised by the more startling effects temperature can have on aircrew in demanding flight or survival conditions and to forget the effects on the groundcrew. In very cold conditions skin can be badly damaged by contact with metal and an instrument or avionics specialist with raw fingertips is a flawed asset. Conversely, sunstroke, dehydration and skin burns from contact with metal airframes heated in the sun are problems which arise under hot conditions. These problems rarely occur on units which are permanently based in either cold or hot conditions; the normal accepted operating and servicing procedures are developed over the years to account for the dangers. The problems emerge when units are redeployed into conditions different from their norm. As in all things to do with aviation, if it is different—take care!

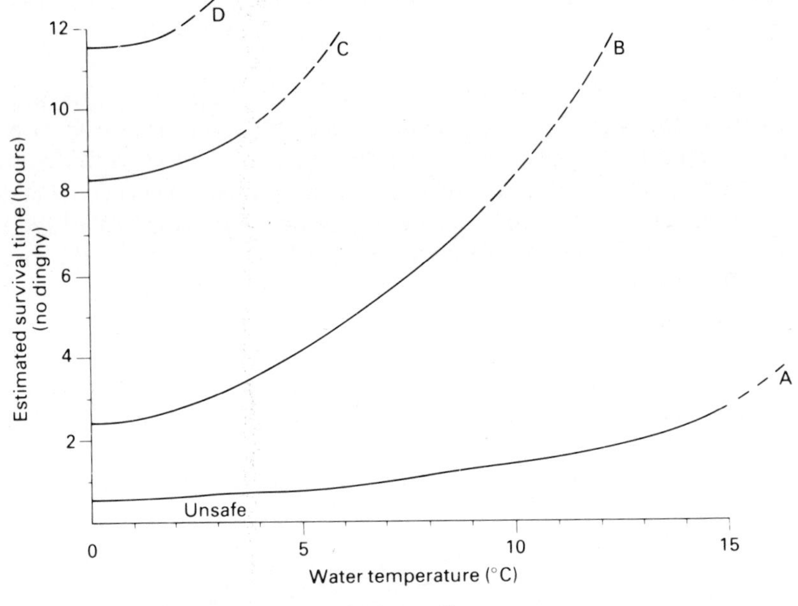

A, Summer AEA (no immersion coverall).
B, Immersion coverall with low insulation.
C, Immersion coverall with medium insulation.
D, Immersion coverall with high insulation.

FIG. 1.13. Survival times in water.

WEATHER COMBINATIONS

More often than not, weather effects will be present in combination. Heavy overcast cloud is often associated with precipitation; continental land masses can give rise to the massive, and potentially dangerous, cumulo-nimbus; low temperature and precipitation gives rise to snow, ice and hail, the latter being quite capable of severely damaging aircraft travelling at high speeds. The combination which gives rise to many problems in the ground-attack role is the coincidence of low cloud and low visibility.

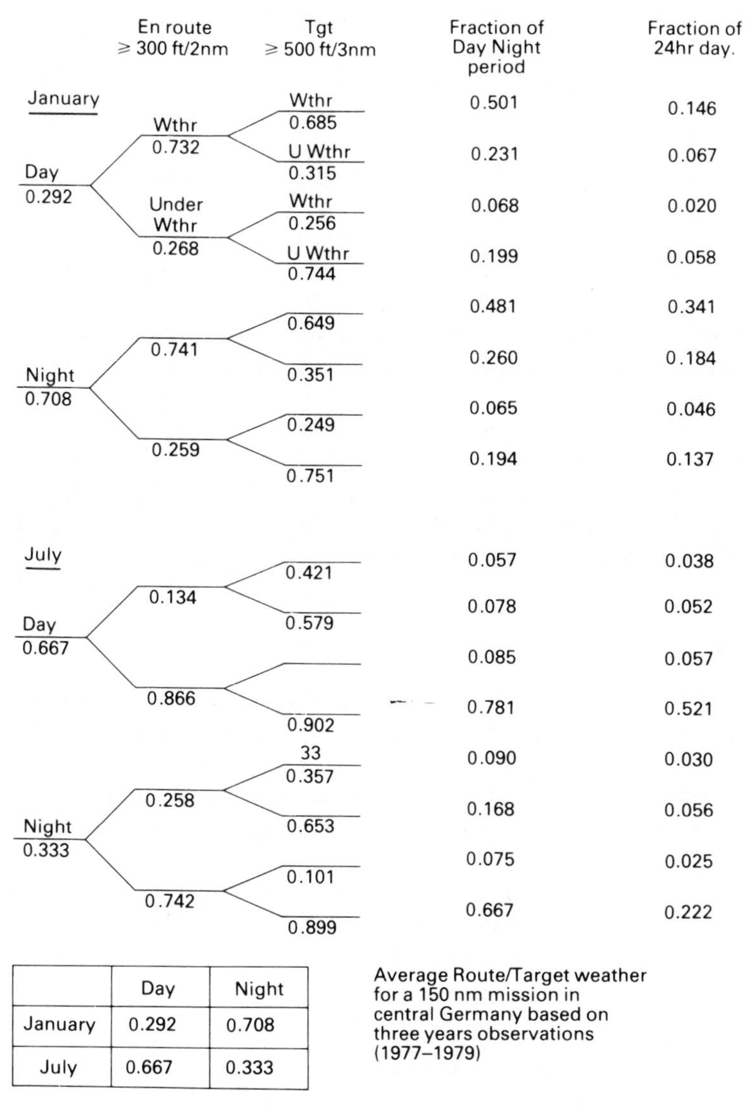

	Day	Night
January	0.292	0.708
July	0.667	0.333

FIG. 1.14. Day and night/summer and winter.

Low cloud in itself is not a major problem, providing there is sufficient ground clearance to enable the route to be flown at the desired height. This clearance does not have to be very great; for example, a pilot trained normally to fly competently at 250 ft should be able to fly operationally in cloud bases of 300 ft. Any such statement must be conditional on other factors; flat or gently rolling terrain would demand smaller margins than heavily mountainous terrain, but visibility is perhaps the most important factor. Good clear visibility beneath a low cloud base provides less problem than sometimes imagined. Conversely, when in-flight visibility is low, then a proportionally higher cloud base is desirable.

In examining weather combinations some work undertaken by the USAF has shown the overall mission effect which can result. In this case three main elements were examined: the proportion of day and night, the probability of experiencing a given *en route* weather state, and the probability of experiencing a certain target weather condition. In the case used here it is assumed that a satisfactory *en route* weather would be a 300-ft cloud base and a 2-nm visibility. In the target area, a better weather condition has been assumed to allow for the requirements of target acquisition and of weapon delivery. It is assumed that in the target area a 500-ft cloud base and a 3-nm visibility is required. The weather statistics were taken from a 3-year reading over an average route of 150 nm in the FRG.

The results shown in Fig. 1.14 highlight some very interesting relationships between seasons, in this case winter (January) and summer (July), and between day and night.

The extraction of day/night data for this particular area of central FRG highlights the point made earlier. In summer, two-thirds of the 24-hr period is 'day' and one-third 'night', while in the winter a little over two-thirds is 'night' and only 7 hr are 'day'. Unlike the other statistics presented, these figures for day/night are not probabilities, they are *certainties.*

ALL-WEATHER

Bearing in mind that the statistics are based on two definitions of all-weather, 200 ft/2 nm en route and 500 ft/3 nm at target, and that the figures will change as the weather conditions specified change, it is instructive to examine the probability of these particular 'all-weather' conditions occurring.

First, consider an aircraft with the bare minimum of mission equipment, generally recognised as a 'day only' capability, and typical of the many thousands of aircraft to be found in the inventories of nations throughout the world. Such aircraft would be unable to safely handle poor *en route* weather and would need good target area weather. They would be ineffective at night. They would be able to operate (Fig. 1.15).

			En route weather		Target weather		Fraction of 24 hr
Season	Day	Night	Under	In	Under	In	
January	.292		.268		.744		.058
July	.667		.866		.902		.521
							Avg 28.95%

FIG. 1.15. Operating time.

By investing in a simple night vision aid such as night vision goggles, the occasions on which the aircraft could be used, enabling as they would, at least transit or *en route* capability, would be as follows (Fig. 1.16).

Season	Day	Night	En route weather		Target weather		Fraction of 24 hr
			Under	In	Under	In	
January	.708		.259		.751		.137
July	.333		.742		.899		.222
							Avg 17.95%

FIG. 1.16. Operating time with night vision equipment.

That is, a total operating time, on average throughout the year, of:

$$28.95\% + 17.95\% = \underline{46.9\%}.$$

If the aircraft is further fitted with an accurate navigation system, it would be possible to navigate *en route* without needing visual contact with the ground, so extending operating time by the amount of time during which the *en route* weather would be below limits. The navigation system referred to here is some way short of a full nav/attack system. It could be a system without any attack facility and could be represented by equipment shortly to be available for use with the US satellite navigation system, the Global Positioning System. This offers great accuracy at low cost; a future system aimed at the yacht market is forecast to market at about US$10,000. Providing the accuracy is good enough and reliable enough, there is no reason why the aircraft cannot be flown at reasonably low levels in a 'poor-man's'—or predicted—terrain-following technique. Operating time is extended as shown in Fig. 1.17.

So, the available operating time of an aircraft can be more than doubled by the incorporation of two *relatively* inexpensive equipments, NVG, which when in full production will probably market at about US$30,000 per helmet set, and GPS, on some similar performing system, at something in the order of $100,000. A doubling of operational availability is impressive enough, but remember that in the winter months the factor is well over a *sevenfold* improvement. In short war scenarios such improvement could make the difference to whether air power could or could not make a meaningful contribution to a winter war. The Ardennes in 1944 is a lesson no airman should forget.

Season	Day	Night	En route weather		Target weather		Fraction of 24 hr	
			Under	In	Under	In		
January	.292			.732	.315		.067	.251
		.708		.741	.351		.184	
July	.667			.134	.579		.052	.108
		.333		.258	.653		.056	
							Avg 17.95%	

FIG. 1.17. Operating time with navigation system.

That is, a total operating time, on average throughout the year, of:

$$28.95\% + 17.95\% + 17.95\% = \underline{64.85\%}.$$

The remaining 35.15 per cent availability becomes progressively more difficult and more expensive to exploit, for it represents the time that the target area is in weather. Two problems have to be solved apart from the overriding requirement to be able to fly a survivable profile in the target area: target acquisition and target attack. In conditions of poor visibility forward-looking infrared devices can greatly improve target-acquisition capabilities, but in the more normally accepted 'all-weather' conditions which may include low cloud and perhaps precipitation, radar is currently the only practical answer. Even this is not straightforward and can call for a balance of judgement between radars with characteristics which give good range and are tolerant of precipitation but lack fine discrimination, and those of shorter range, degraded by precipitation, but capable of detecting the smaller military targets. These later radars include those in the millimetric bands. Such radars are seldom cheap.

Acquisition is only the start of the attack process, and the radar needs to be integrated into an attack system if a blind attack is to be executed. Such integrated navigation and attack systems, capable of blind attack, and the operational profile necessary for survival are at the top end of the avionic spectrum in complexity and cost. They are typified by the systems to be found in the F-111, Tornado, SU-24, Fencer and, in advanced form, in the B-1. In aircraft such as these it is not uncommon to find that the cost of the mission avionics is over a third of the total cost of the aircraft as a whole, and most commentators agree that this proportion will increase rather than decrease with time. The last 35.15 per cent of combat availability is a costly business to exploit.

'LIES, DAMN LIES AND STATISTICS'

The purpose of presenting the statistics and the conclusions drawn from them has been to illustrate how the environment must be taken as the first constant in any new design study, but, more importantly, to illustrate how thinking should proceed towards the determination of a true cost-effective solution. At many stages further downstream in the life of a project, extensive, and sometimes amazingly expensive, studies are conducted to try and find the most cost-effective route, but much of this sterling effort can be in vain if the essential first step, the acknowledgement of the natural physical conditions, has been avoided in the earlier stages.

Before even considering the physical environment, the operators must specify clearly what their requirements are. In the example used above it was assumed that a target area weather of 500 ft and 3 nm was necessary. In consequence it transpired that on some one-third of the total available time these conditions would not be present and could lead to the requirement for expensive nav/attack systems. If, however, the operators were prepared to accept 200-ft and 2-nm target area weather, the 35.15 per cent gap would reduce appreciably as would the case for the more sophisticated systems. In the extreme 'all-weather' case, cloud bases barely off the ground and visibilities below fog limits, highly if not fully-automated attacks have to be conducted using the most sophisticated equipment, but such conditions exist only 2–3 per cent of the time. Is it cost-effective to increase the cost of an aircraft by 50 per cent to handle conditions which exist for only 2–3 per cent of the time?

In general, therefore, the airman is a creature of his environment and he must understand it, but he must also be told about it, and that is the task of the much abused men of the meteorological services. There has always been somewhat of a 'love–hate' relationship between aviator and 'met-man' in the past—it may well continue in the future—even though as his task is eased by modern technology the movement will be towards more 'love' and less 'hate'. A healthy trend.

Forecasting the weather is not the easiest of professions, and even with the new computers and satellite information some would suggest that there is still a touch of art to the science. A particular burden of the met-man is that his customers tend to take his correct forecast for granted, but remember those which went wrong, probably because they are the ones which caused fright, pain or grief. The really memorable met forecasts are those that went wrong and too many become enshrined in folklore and magnified with the telling.

Despite modern aids, there must still be a certain irreducible level of uncertainty able to be achieved in forecasting the future. Some errors are more important than others in their effect. A cloud base forecast for 3,500 ft which actually turns out to be at 3,100 ft is something which may go unremarked; a 400-ft error of minor significance, but a forecast of 500 ft which turns out to be 100 ft is a 400-ft error of quite different significance. Coastal effects can be very difficult to predict, and European shorelines facing prevailing winds from the still sparsely measured Atlantic wastes present particular difficulties. In such situations local knowledge cannot be ignored. One base in the United Kingdom was saved from embarrassment with a new aircraft type when a local workman expressed surprise that the aircraft were not back yet because "yon lighthouse has the haze over it". The last, hastily recalled, aircraft landed downwind ahead of the unforecast fog rolling in from the sea, an event which surprised operator and met-man alike, but taken as a self-evident truth by the local populace.

Can the weather be used operationally? Some would paint a scenario which suggests that it could, but reality casts doubt over this. If surprise is to be obtained, the warning time to the opposition must be kept to a minimum. If preparation time was short, then operations could perhaps be synchronised with a weather pattern, good or bad. But major offensives with large forces take many days if not weeks to prepare, and forecasting the weather that far ahead is still unreliable. To hold a force at high readiness waiting for suitable weather is weakening to men and material and risks pre-emption. The agonising debate in 1944 at 'Overlord', the Normandy invasion, where the crucial item was the weather, had to take just such factors into account. Interestingly, the met-man in the hot seat at the time has since emerged as somewhat of an heroic figure.

The weather or, perhaps more widely, the environment may well be considered in the more macro, or seasonal, sense. An attacker may reason that he should avoid the monsoon; that his air power was significant, therefore the long days of summer were better than the restricted flying days of winter; that an armoured force might be better served by the frozen ground of winter than the thaw and muds of spring; that ice-free approaches to his ports were essential to his naval plans. Even though seasonal forecasting is safer, it still has its pitfalls. The clear, sunny days of a December or January; the snow in May—there are enough examples. Advocates of air power could ponder profitably on the weather effect on two decisive battles; the Battle of Britain fought in conditions of a splendid English summer—was it only radar which aided the interceptions; and the Battle of the Bulge in the Ardennes, where the air power answer to initiative and audacity was removed from the equation for the crucial early days by persistent clinging fog and low cloud.

It pays to both understand the environment and to respect it; it has a painful bite!

2

Aircraft Design

Great developments have taken place in aviation over a short space of time. Some of the best brains in science and engineering have been attracted to the field. Its history is full of famous names, men and women of great innovation, or courage, or brilliance, or combinations of all three. It continues to be a dynamic and exciting field, and of the two areas of concern in this volume, aircraft and operations, the greatest impact currently must be conceded to the designer, for it is here where developments are proceeding apace and are having such a dominating effect on the operator. There was a time, and we may be at the turn of that time, when the operator specified what he wanted and the designer produced equipment to meet the specification. Now, increasingly, technology is leaping ahead and the operator is having to hasten after it lest his thinking be overtaken by events. In the past some have argued that tactics have driven technology; increasingly, technology is now driving tactics. Discourse between the designer and the operator is more vital than it has ever been before and both need to have a greater understanding of the other's constraints and opportunities.

'Dynamism' and 'excitement' are words which can be excused in a field where such amazing progress has been made within the lifespan of many still alive. The first flight of the Wright brothers took place at Kitty Hawk in December 1903. It consisted of little more than a hop; a distance of 852 ft and the craft was in the air under its own power for merely 59 sec. By October 1905 the brothers had demonstrated flight in a circle, travelling 24½ miles in 38 min at Dayton, Ohio. By 1908 this improvement had been bettered impressively and the Michelin Trophy was won with a flight of 77 miles in a time of 2 hr 20 min. Although Wilbur, the older of the two brothers, died in 1912 before the full impetus was under way, Orville lived until 1948 and saw the birth of the jet engine and the start of man's flirtation with supersonic flight. He had witnessed two World Wars, the second of which saw air forces win their place in their own right alongside the other two established arms; he saw air power used strategically, culminating in the two ultimate demonstrations of its effectiveness at Hiroshima and at Nagasaki.

Within 25 years of the first flight, aircraft were carrying fare-paying passengers. Within 50 years aircraft were travelling faster than the speed of sound and within 75 years man's almost daily exploits in space had ceased to arouse undue interest. The modest powered flight by the pioneer American was surpassed in 1962 when another American, John Glenn, travelled some 81,000 miles in less than 5 hr at an altitude approaching 160 miles. No mean achievement over what in historical terms is so short a time.

In military operations the use of the aircraft, its systems and its weapons must be considered in their entirety. Each aspect interfaces with the other, and the total is indeed greater than the sum of the parts. Each deserve textbooks in their own right and the intention here is merely to look at trends from the eye of the operator, looking for those indicators which show where changes in operational thinking can yield profit, or even where change may be forced upon the operator regardless of his wishes.

AIRFRAME

In the past, design was constrained by the properties of the available materials and in the early days wood and doped fabric had to suffice. Since then there have been two types of improvement: the evolutionary, where steady gain has been made over a period of time and the difference between the older aluminium alloys and those in popular use today give an insight to that process; and the revolutionary, or step improvements, where major changes have come about over a short period. Of these, the move from wood to metal stands out, as does the use of monocoque and stressed skin construction which permitted in turn the move from biplanes to monoplanes. As more engine power became available, so the need arose to advance aerodynamically to better utilise the higher speeds available and a series of innovative wing designs began to evolve. Of major impact was the use of the swept wing to delay the effects of compressibility. There are many varieties based on this theme; the variable geometry, or swing wing, attempts to match any particular flight condition with a sweep tailored exactly. The success of this solution depends on the extent that the complex aerodynamics over extended speed ranges can be accurately predicted, and on the skill of the engineer in ensuring that the weight penalty paid for the mechanism is not so great that the advantage gained in one area is not lost in another. The complexity inherent in this solution should not be underestimated. Wing carry-through boxes have not only to be strong enough to withstand the normal transverse loads but must also withstand a variety of torsional loads as the wing takes the weight at different angles of sweep. It is not only the swinging mechanism which accounts for the weight penalty. On a combat aircraft utilising pylons, each pylon must be kept in line with the airflow as the wing sweeps, and this demands more complicated mechanisms than would be required if the wing was fixed. The same applies to the design and construction of most of the moving parts; the aerodynamics of flaps and slats have to be tolerant of a wider range of airflow direction than would be the case if the wing did not swing. The F-111, for example, has no less than thirty-two movable trailing edge surfaces. The penalty for resorting to a swing-wing solution is in the order of 10 per cent by weight and probably as high as 15 per cent by cost. Penalties in operational capability on the one hand, and in its implication on total fleet size on the other, demand that swing wings are used only when other solutions are incapable of producing the desired results.

Increasingly, other solutions are becoming available or are showing promise, solutions which efficiently produce high lift coefficients and are tolerant of wide speed ranges. A departure from the more normal rearward-swept wing is the forward-swept wing. In this approach the problems of the conventional swept wing are all but reversed. The spanwise flow of air and the turbulence which causes the aft-swept wing tip to stall and to induce pitch-up is reversed in the case of the forward-swept wing and the spanwise flow is towards the root of the wing, so improving lateral control. Previously, using the materials available, the problem of preventing the forward-swept wing bending in such a way as to cause the tips to stall through an increased angle of attack could not be satisfactorily solved. With the advent of the new composite materials, the wing can be constructed to prevent bending under load in the undesirable sense and divergence at high angles of attack can be avoided. By careful matching of a forward-swept design with the use of canards, the airflow resulting from the forward canard can be used to mitigate the turbulence at the wing–fuselage interface and so reduce drag and enhance lift. A full-sized flying test aircraft utilising the forward-swept wing has been built and will add much to the understanding of the complex design problems of exploiting the distortions of an airframe through flight loading.

Another solution to the tailoring of a wing to different flight conditions is the 'Mission Adaptive Wing' (MAW). In this approach the shape of the camber of the wing is changed in flight by the use of extensive moving surfaces at the leading and trailing edges. For a high lift condition, at take-off or in combat, the forward and trailing edges will be drooped in the same way as conventional slats and flaps are positioned for take-off. At cruise the wing will assume a normal profile and at penetration at high speed, and possibly at low level where high lift can give undesirable gust loadings, the wing can be tailored to produce only the minimum of lift required. This not only improves the ride quality but in reducing the lift-induced drag can also contribute to increased range. Combined with a computer-based flight control system using sensors of the flight condition it is possible to see the wing being continually programmed for the optimal shape to meet the pilot's demands. This would result in carefree operation from the pilot's viewpoint if the promise can be realised. As with the swing wing, there is a penalty to pay in complexity and weight, for unlike conventional flaps and slats the moving parts of a MAW must be strong enough to withstand movement in the conditions of high-speed flight and to remain well sealed against any through-aerofoil air flow which would negate many of the advantages. Together, these present a formidable engineering problem.

The Harrier has demonstrated the ability to use vectored engine thrust to provide lift. In this extreme case the thrust available exceeds the weight of the aircraft by the required surplus, of about 1.2 to 1, and vertical operations are possible. During the transition between vertical and conventional flight the aircraft goes through a period where the total lift requirement is provided partly by wing lift and partly by engine thrust. The same principle has been found to work in combat where the technique of 'Vectoring In Forward Flight', VIFF-ing, has been used with some limited success. This enables the turn rate of the aircraft to be temporarily increased by changing the thrust vector of the engine to increase the effective lift vector. Designs for the future are now being considered which capitalise on the same principle, and vectoring nozzles on more conventional designs, two-dimensional or even three-dimensional, are part of an approach to give aircraft increased freedom of manoeuvre.

The penalties of increased weight, complexity, and thereby cost for developments such as the swing wing, the forward-swept wing, the MAW, and vectored thrust can be defended, providing it is the only way to provide the increased lift required. But there are more conventional ways of greatly increasing lift. The formulae for lift is:

$$\text{Lift} = C_l \tfrac{1}{2} p V^2 S$$

where C_l is the lift coefficient of the wing,
p is the air density (0.00024 at sea level),
V is the speed of the airflow (in ft/sec),
S is the area of the wing (in ft^2).

It can be seen from the formulae for lift that as the airspeed factor is a squared function the total lift is heavily dependent on the airflow over the aerofoil. Conventionally, this is provided by moving the whole airframe through the air, but the same effect as far as the aerofoil is concerned is produced if the local airflow over the wing can be increased. This can be done in a variety of ways, the two most popular being by using engine exhaust blown from slots along the span of the wing to provide a combination of boundary layer control, which delays the advent of turbulent flow and increases lift, and directs high-speed airflow over the aerofoil section. An alternative method is that used on the YC-15 project, and planned for use on the proposed C-17, and involves using the engine exhaust to flow over extended flap surfaces, so producing the increased airflow and inducing a faster flow over the main wing structure.

A study conducted recently concluded that by using upper surface blowing by direct engine exhaust, and by utilising span-wide rear blowing to control circulation, lift coefficients could be more than tripled. The aircraft used in the study, the Lockheed S-3A, showed that the present take-off lift coefficient, in the order of 1.5, could be increased to over 8 with the use of the two techniques. Take-off speed at a weight of 30,000 lb could be halved from something over 100 kts to a little over 50 kts. An advantage is that the system would require no moving parts and reliability should be high.

The amount of lift required is dependent upon the weight of the aircraft and its payload. Weight reduction by the use of materials which are light and strong is therefore a very profitable course to pursue. Recently there have been many important advances in this area and the development in a steady progression of the aluminium derivatives and alloys has already been mentioned. The development of the very strong and light aluminium–lithium alloys show that it will be some time, if ever, before aluminium loses its favoured place as an aircraft construction material. It is not only the lightness of the material which matters, but also the form in which it is fabricated to obtain the required strength and torsional stiffness. Honeycomb structures, two thin sheets of material bonded together either side of a light honeycomb core, can be very effective in providing light and stiff structures. Although offering great advantages to the designer, care must be taken to ensure that the maintenance engineer, who will have to repair battle-damaged aircraft, can work the more exotic structures in the field.

Carbon-fibre composite materials offer great strength at low weights and will play an important part in future airframes. Already the cost of the raw material is starting to fall from its very high initial price and much work is under way to attempt to reduce the presently manpower-intensive, and thereby expensive, method of laying-up. Perhaps robotics may have an application here. There is also some concern to be eased about satisfactory inspection of the finished product and there are fears to be stilled in the matter of battle-damage repair, particularly where impact damage could perhaps cause an element of delamination or internal weakening which might be difficult to detect in the field using non-specialist test equipment.

Both honeycomb techniques and the new composites point the way to the increasing use of adhesives. An older and more conventional airframe will show the extensive riveting in the structure. This is both manpower-intensive and works against the natural desire of a good designer not to pierce metal unless it is essential. Pulled rivets and crack propagation from the perforations in conventional structures remain an everyday problem. A good bond with modern two-part adhesives can offer attractions, not least that of a continuous solid join between two sheets, easing the problem of corrosion and carrying structural loads more evenly. Testing, durability and in-field maintenance must be satisfied before the technique can be applied widely, but it is clear that it will become more prevalent in the future. Adhesives are widely used already in battle-damage repair techniques where a strong, quick, if sometimes unglamorous, repair is needed. Some test specimens repaired with copious quantities of modern adhesives have proved to be stronger than the surrounding original structure.

Another manufacturing technique which will have its effect is super-plastically-formed diffusion-bonded titanium alloys. Such material can be constructed in complex shapes of great strength and can offer considerable savings in manufacture. The shapes required by new intake designs—and a study of the F-16 intake will give an insight to the problem, and the demands made by design for 'stealth', where sharp corners which form radar reflectors are avoided—indicate that new techniques such as the super-plastically-formed alloys will have a role to play. Yet again, the difficulty of repairing battle damage on such complicated shapes presents a problem to the field engineer and the more complex shapes may have to be repaired by replacement, an option demanding large and costly inventories.

The quiet revolution in aerodynamics, structures and materials has placed a great burden on the designer, and if demanding military specifications are to be met, he must optimise to the full the capability which computer aided design (CAD) offers. The faster processing times and the greater core capability of modern computers is allowing some of the hard graft of design work to be eased and options examined much faster than has been possible in the past. This is particularly the case in the field of fluid dynamics, which largely determines the efficiency of the new range of wings.

PROPULSION

The factor which delayed sustained flight more than any other was the lack of a reliable and lightweight power plant. Successful experiments with gliders had taken place before the Wrights' first flight, but they had to design and build their own engine before they could get aloft and stay aloft. It was a modest affair, a mere 12 hp produced from 180 lb weight. Its power-to-weight ratio of 1:15, compared to the thrust-to-weight ratios of 8:1 today, gives some measure of the success of the engine designer over the years. The main progress towards improvement has been along three lines, and these remain true today and seem set to be so for the foreseeable future; to obtain higher thrust or power levels, to reduce fuel consumption, and of great importance to civilian or military operator alike, but particularly so for those who fly single-engine machines, improved reliability and maintainability.

High-thrust engines are a regular sight around the airports of the world. Engines of 50,000 lb thrust or more are used on a variety of aircraft, and the designers see no major problem in extending the range into the 60,000-lb bracket. These large and commercially sound engines owe much of their success to the advent of high-bypass ratios, that is the relationship of the amount of air that passes through the high-pressure combustor and turbine core of the engine and that which passes through the first-stage, usually rather large, fan at the front. The 1960s saw the initial development of bypass designs giving some 15–25 per cent better fuel consumption from bypass ratios as low as 2 : 1, but it was in the 1970s when bypass ratios as high as 8 : 1 resulted in improvements in fuel consumption of 25–35 per cent. Following the oil crisis in 1973 and the start of the rise in fuel costs, from the prevailing rate of about 10 cents a gallon to a figure in the order of $1 a gallon in 1980, it might be thought that it was fortunate that the high-bypass development came when it did.

Generally as the bypass ratio increases, so fuel consumption decreases, assuming a given core size. In turn, the effectiveness of the core, where the work is done on the air flowing through the engine, is largely determined by the efficiency the heat produced from the fuel can be transferred to the airflow. This rests upon the properties of the materials used, and the search for materials to withstand the very high temperatures involved continues. The ability of the materials to withstand the very high temperatures can be enhanced by using compressor bleed air from the engine to cool the hotter parts, and it is not unusual to find air of 1,000°F being used to keep turbine metal temperatures in the bearable range around 1,800°F. This enables gas stream temperatures to be used around 2,500°F, so improving the thermodynamic efficiency, while improvements in the specialist science of turbine aerodynamics permit the use of higher compressor and turbine speeds which in turn better exploit the energy in the flow.

The high cost of developing new engines prevents them being replaced regularly by new designs. That cost was vividly demonstrated by the near collapse in the early seventies of the respected and not unsubstantial firm of Rolls-Royce when the development costs of their now successful RB-211 engine nearly destroyed them. The trend will be towards derivatives of engines over extended periods of time, with those derivatives being produced in a variety of forms over wide power brackets. Changes in the engines will generally be directed towards improvements in economy or reliability, while the engine will be matched to meet specific requirements. The opportunity which this trend offers to the military is the possibility of commonality of major engine components over a fleet of types, with the engine tuned to each but allowing the saving of radically different training centres and stores inventories. There is a strong move in the US military towards this approach.

When new engines are developed, there will be an attempt to achieve similar or better fuel economy, but by the use of lower bypass ratios, higher overall pressure ratios through the engine and higher turbine inlet temperatures. There will also be a drive towards making engines smaller and with many fewer moving parts than was the case before. Size, particularly weight and frontal area, are important factors in both commercial and military operations. In the air transport operation there is little to be gained by a massive investment in a new engine to improve the specific fuel consumption if the result is an increased cowling dimension which, on a long flight, may cost far more fuel because of its drag than the expensive new engine could possibly save. The trend towards greater simplicity of design can be seen by the comparison of two engines each producing very similar thrust ratings, the old J79 engine of F-4 Phantom fame and an engine of the fifties, and the new F404 engine of the F-18 born of the 1970s.

After considering the big fan engines with their first stages constrained by the ducting of the engine cowling, it is not a large step to orientate to the use of a propeller rather than a fan on the turbine core engine. The move back towards propellers gained impetus amongst the scares of fuel famine or prohibitively high fuel costs arising from the 1973 oil crisis. A decade later, enough work has been done to suggest that there is a benefit to be had in certain applications, and this is made possible by work done on propeller designs which can accept the high Mach numbers necessary to make commercial and military sense. Not surprisingly, when it is considered that the blade of a propeller suffers the same high-speed aerodynamic effects as does the wing of an aircraft, the new designs are far different from those of old, with the straight blade replaced by highly curved or swept blades to delay the onset of compressibility. Small wind-tunnel models have been tested successfully and must now be examined in the 10–15 ft diameter form that they will have to assume to be effective in service. Another area which will require development is that of power transmission. The engines of today produce much more power than those of yesteryear, and while power transmission in the true sense is not a problem in a jet engine it assumes far more importance when the high rotational speeds of the turbines have to be reduced to the speeds which can be absorbed by the propeller. Current gearboxes and reduction gears capable of handling about 5,000 hp will have to be improved upon by factors as much as 3, and that presents no small challenge. Realising the technical problems and the weight penalties of reduction gears of this magnitude, at least one engine manufacturer is trying to drive the propeller directly from the free-flow air in the turbine area of the engine, but this too presents formidable problems of engineering and of matching the engine, the latter so important to its efficiency.

The gain to be had if the prop-jet can be successfully launched is impressive. An advanced design of Pratt & Whitney, the STS589, is forecast to produce a specific fuel consumption of 0.52 at Mach 0.8 at 35,000 ft, and this compares impressively with the 0.58 of the new generation PW2037 turbo-fan to be fitted to the Boeing 757 and C-17, and even more so to the JT8D engine, which distinguished itself so well on a variety of aircraft of the sixties and seventies, of 0.82.

The difference between 0.58 and 0.52 may not sound a great deal and might raise the question of whether the resources put into its achievement could not be better expended elsewhere. But that difference to an airline flying regular long-haul routes, and utilising their aircraft towards the upper end of current airline practice, could make the difference of well over $6,000 per flight or over $1.5 million a year. When it is realised that over 600 Boeing 747s, 400 DC-10s and 275 Tristars have been built, the sum savings assume impressive proportions.

The big fan engines and the prop-jets do not have an application to fighter, fighter-bomber and bomber aircraft, at least not those which have to penetrate enemy territory or need high performance for the air combat mission. In the early days such aircraft were powered by pure jets, and when the power requirements continued to rise they were met by afterburning, or the introduction of fuel into the jet pipe of the engine and the adjustment of the nozzle to produce greater thrust. This has always been, and continues to be, a very expensive way of augmenting thrust. In the late sixties the advent of the F-4K and M for the RAF and the introduction of the F-111 into the USAF saw the first application of afterburning to bypass engines, the Rolls-Royce Spey in the case of the F-4 and the TF30 in the F-111. Later the TurboUnion RB199 was introduced to power the European multi-role aircraft, popularly known as the Tornado. These three aircraft demonstrate some interesting points.

A more economical engine is not in itself a good thing if it brings in its wake compensating disadvantages. In the case of the RAF F-4, the political decision to Anglicise the aircraft to the maximum to save foreign exchange costs caused the aircraft to have the well-proven J79 engine removed and the Rolls-Royce Spey engine fitted in its place. Rolls-Royce brilliantly solved the problem of afterburning the bypass Spey and, at first examination, it seemed that the RAF would get not only the economy of the Spey, which was very good, but with the use of the afterburner would possess the most powerful F-4 of the stable. To fit the larger Spey to the airframe, however, required the intakes to be enlarged to accept a greater airflow of the bypass engine and at the rear the larger Spey jet pipes necessitated the rear fuselage to be made deeper. An aircraft carefully designed for flight in the Mach 2 regime takes ill to such cavalier treatment and the promise of the Spey F-4 was not realised despite its paper attraction. The RAF ended up with the most powerful, but slowest, F-4 of all, and it is a tribute to the aircraft that it has proved so effective in service despite that. The lesson is clear; combat aircraft are entities, not a collection of components assembled in close formation.

The cases of the F-111 and the Tornado are more interesting in the lesson which they can teach. Both were evolved as multi-role aircraft which presents the designer with a major engine problem. For the long-range penetration mission high engine efficiency is required to achieve the range so essential to that role. Consequently, as a turbine engine operates most efficiently at the higher rpm, this leads to the selection of small engines working near their non-afterburned or 'dry' maximum. Take-off and combat thrust have to be produced by afterburning, but the long-duration cruise is done most efficiently. The dominant cruise requirement also leads towards high-bypass ratios to improve specific fuel consumption.

Conversely, for the fighter combat role the emphasis swings to high thrust; more of a pure-jet afterburned engine would be the designer's first choice for such an aircraft, and the bypass ratios for engines designed with the air superiority role in mind show the trend; the F100 engine of the F-15 and F-16 and the F404 engine of the F-18 have bypass ratios of 0.63 and 0.34 respectively. The F101 engine designed for the B-1 strategic bomber, on the other hand, has a bypass ratio of 2.01. It is hardly surprising, therefore, to find the compromise or multi-role aircraft between these two poles with the TF30 engine of the F-111 at a bypass ratio of 1.10 and the RB199 of the Tornado greater than 1.

It is also of interest that both *multi-role* designs have fallen some way short of their expectations. While the F-111 excels in the role of fast, long-range penetrator, it has not been introduced into the fighter role at all. The Tornado has also shown itself well in the penetration role, but lacks the range originally expected, and the development of a fighter version has already started a debate about re-engining and has called for a new radar, fuselage and cockpit. Both multi-role aircraft, one a product of the might of the US industry, no mean giant, and the other the product of the European amalgam, have failed to achieve a genuine multi-role capability. Yet those aircraft which remain in the memory as excellent multi-role aircraft are those which have started life on single-role specification. From World War II perhaps the Mosquito, certainly shortly thereafter the Canberra and the Hunter from the United Kingdom, dwarfed by the F-4 Phantom and now the promise of the F-16 and F-15 from the United States, and not forgetting the stable of long-lived Soviet designs of which the Fitter and the MiG-23 stand out. Is the lesson here that we have yet to advance our technology to the point where conflicting requirements can be satisfactorily welded into one design? Or is multi-role capability a myth? Or are there other ways of achieving it, ways approaching the problem from another standpoint? An electronics standpoint perhaps?

ELECTRONICS

In aerodynamics and thermodynamics there have been a series of breakthroughs amongst the general thrust of rapid development, but both are eclipsed by the advance in electronics. The possibilities opened by the new capabilities for data and signal processing mark the advent of both the 'smart' aircraft and the 'smart' weapon. The opportunity exists to make advances in capability barely dreamt of two decades ago.

The electronic revolution has come about with the advent of the computer and the advances made in that area over the years. Early computers were massive devices regularly filling rooms, and some buildings, to produce performances which would now be considered modest. They were expensive, slow and cumbersome. The trend is demonstrated well by the development of the pocket calculator. When first introduced, and performing little more than the basic arithmetical functions, they were bulky and sold at £100 or more. Despite inflation, that face value today buys a programmable calculator, with arithmetical, geometric and statistical functions. Over the years computer power has increased, size and cost has decreased, and the combination has found a home in an ever-increasing range of applications.

In military application the growth of computer usage has been impressive. The advantage of using digital devices in weapon systems rather than the less accurate and unreliable analogue systems was quickly recognised and the size and weight savings in many aeronautical applications offered real advantage. Modern aircraft like the F-16 were designed to exploit the electronic revolution to the full. The weapons system relies upon extensive use of on-board computers but so also does the flight control system which uses computers to control the dynamically unstable design through a fly-by-wire system.

The advantage offered by the computer in this area is indicative of the very high return in performances which computers (which will be used as a shorthand for 'data processing') offer. Up to quite recently the designer was limited to production of dynamically stable designs. In such a design it is necessary to ensure that the lift produced from the wing acted through a point which was behind the centre of gravity of the aircraft. To produce a balance of forces, the tailplane had to produce a negative value of lift, or download. Clearly the deliberate production of download in a structure designed to lift itself into the air was a contradiction, albeit a necessary one.

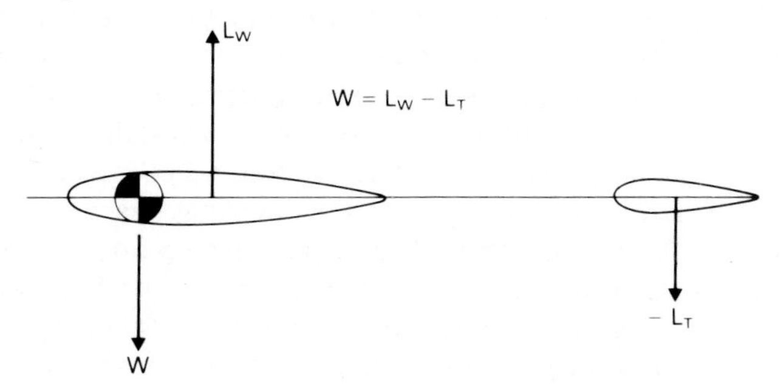

FIG. 2.1. Balance of forces on a stable design.

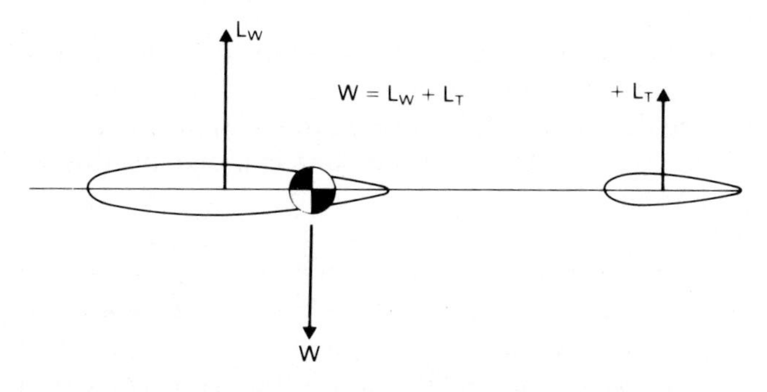

FIG. 2.2. Balance of forces on an unstable design.

If, however, the first excursion of a dynamically unstable aircraft can be detected in its initial stages and a correcting movement of the control surfaces instigated quickly, then the dynamic instability can be controlled. As the aircraft is in a condition of always wanting to enter an excursion, it can be seen that its response to any control movement is rapid, an ideal characteristic for a combat aircraft, but the advantages go much further than that. If the balance of the aircraft can be controlled electronically, then the lift vector can be allowed to precede the weight vector, so allowing the balancing movement of the tailplane to be positive instead of negative. The total lift of the aircraft can thereby be improved.

This advantage can start a virtuous circle. Already better control response has been achieved, but now for a constant lifting area of wing and tailplane more lift can be provided, or, an important corollary, for a given total lift requirement the lifting surfaces can be reduced, which in turn reduces weight, drag and structure cost. As weight and drag are reduced, so are the demands on engine power, and savings can be looked for in power plant size and weight and in the fuel fraction to support it. In all a most profitable course for the designer, all made possible by the use of the computer in the control system.

In this example the computer is applied to aerodynamic problems, but its use in weapon and navigation systems is now widespread. In this field it allows many more inputs to be handled than possible with analogue systems with the resultant improvement of accuracy. This is particularly so because the digital functioning of the computer allows inputs to be tested against predetermined criteria to determine whether the signal is inaccurate or illogical. It is difficult to conduct such filtering in analogue systems. This filtering process is being used increasingly in modern systems, and the trend for the future is for it to increase.

The use of the calculating function of the computer is self-evident, but less so is the capability to store information in the form of onboard databases. There are a variety of roles where large databases are required. To a pilot a hand-held map is a navigational database. In its shape, colour and markings it is designed to interface its information to the human brain. Where such navigational data needs to be interfaced to a digital computer, the form of the map must be made compatible with the requirements of the computer. So were born digital maps, and with them the ability to collect information on terrain, shape, height and nature from surveillance systems directly in digital form. In many respects, taking the need for the somewhat restricted human perception from the requirement the problems of database form is eased.

Once a navigational database, or electronic map, is available and can be carried in aircraft or missile, then by sensing the terrain being overflown by radar, video or infrared means and comparing the sensor output with the stored data, an accurate position can be determined. The use of similar techniques in cruise missiles is now commonplace, and the extension of its use into manned aircraft logically cannot be far removed.

An extension of the technique is scene-matching, and this can be used to obtain accurate terminal impacts. It is necessary to have stored an accurate 'picture' of the desired target area, and the weapon system needs to know where exactly on that target area an impact is desired. By sensing the target area in the terminal dive by whatever system is appropriate and, as before, comparing the desired picture with the received picture, the missile can be guided until a match occurs and this is maintained to impact. Very high levels of accuracy are possible with scene-matching techniques.

Another example of the use of an airborne database might be in an electronic support aircraft or in radar warning equipment fitted to penetrating aircraft. In these cases it is necessary to take the received radar signal, analyse it and compare its parameters with the stored characteristics of known enemy transmissions. The profusion of radars operating on the battlefield and beyond calls for an extensive database. It is important to be able to update and extend the database in the shortest possible time under operational conditions when an enemy might reasonably be expected to use frequencies previously kept secret and to attempt to change the characteristics of known equipments.

From these two restricted examples it can be seen that the modern weapon system is highly computer-dependent and is likely in the future to be more so than today. A US assessment suggests that there will be a twenty-five-fold increase in the use of embedded computers in aircraft, missiles and other equipment in a period of only a little more than a decade. This startling fact must give pause for thought by defence managers and economists alike, for it points to the added complexity and cost of modern defence systems.

There exists a myth about cost. The cost of computers has indeed fallen and in the electronics industry there tends to be a cost relationship quite unlike those in other fields where cost escalation is the norm. It does not mean, however, that the cost of military avionics or electronics is reducing; on the contrary, in general it is increasing, much in line with other military hardware. This is because, although the cost of doing any particular function is reducing, the designers and air staffs are exploiting the new capability on offer and are asking for ever more capability. If requirements now were similar to those in the fifties, it would be cheaper; but the requirement now is for what is likely to be possible in the nineties, and that is expensive. The cost of functions has reduced, but more and more functions are being demanded.

Even so, care must be taken when talking about cost. If the use of £1 million worth of avionics so improves the bombing accuracy that only five aircraft worth £20 million need to be despatched to a target when ten would have been required before, then at 10 per cent attrition four times as much has been saved after the first raid than has been invested in the improved system.

This changing pattern is also bringing in its wake other problems. While the cost of hardware is generally reducing in relative terms, function for function, the enormous capacity of the new computers bring with them the problem of programming. Here is seen a quite marked reversal of the cost profile. At first, high-cost, low-capacity computers required only limited and simple programs. Now, highly capable computers require extensive and complex programs. The trend is seen clearly in the civilian sector, where software houses are a growth industry. In the military the need for software support is not so fully realised as perhaps it should be, and many air forces are operating advanced electronic equipment without any depth of software support or, in some cases, software expertise. The problem of retaining trained computer software experts under military pay scales when the pull from the civilian sector is so strong drives most air forces to rely heavily on contractor support for this vital service, but this may have to be looked upon further if this expensive service drives life-cycle costs to levels which question the affordability of the equipment in the first place. This is no minor matter; some estimates suggest that shortly the USAF will be spending 10 per cent of its total equipment budget upon software support for its computers both on the ground and those embedded computers in the airborne equipment. Much of the impetus for the development of the new computer language ADA was the attempt to reduce the costs associated with the abundance of languages which massively increased training costs and called for expensive buffer equipment to interface one equipment with another. It is likely to be an internationally accepted language in a few years time.

The speed at which a computer works is of great interest to the designer of air systems. It is easy to see that the pilot of an aircraft travelling at 600 kts cannot wait long for data before its value is greatly diminished. More so for a missile travelling at Mach 2.5 engaging a head-on target travelling at Mach 1.5. More impressive, the anti-ballistic missile heading at Mach 5 or 6 to intercept a tactical ballistic missile entering the atmosphere at speeds in the order of Mach 22. The closure speeds are very high, and slow computation of complex interception algorithms can mean the difference between a kill and a miss.

It is the demand for more compact, reliable and speedy data processing that is providing much of the drive towards the Very High Speed Integrated Circuit (VHSIC) programme in the United States and elsewhere. The VHSIC performance could provide a step increase in electronic capability which some equate to the effect that the swing wing had on aerodynamics. VHSIC could result in miniaturised integrated circuitry capable of processing data up to 100 times faster than current equipments, and when combined with some advanced architectures speeds even greater than this are more than possible. Indeed, designers are now at the point where they may be limited only by the speed of the electrons through the material of the devices, and one of the attractions of greater miniaturisation is that the electrons have less distance to travel in the smaller component. Consequently, wafers of silicon or gallinium arsenide as thin as 1.25 microns are used as a base on which electronic circuits are printed, and designers are already looking forward to the time when sub-micron wafers will be available. Some scientists go further still and predict that the only physical limitation which will eventually stop progress in this area will be that caused by the size of the atom itself.

A further advantage falling from VHSIC design is that because each VHSIC chip can perform so many functions it can reduce the number of separate circuit boards now used to perform similar tasks. This in turn results in a marked reduction in connections, and it is in the pins and the connectors of electronic equipment that so many faults occur. The USAF have estimated that between 70 and 75 per cent of all maintenance on avionics involves pins and plugs—the places where connections are made. There is some truth in the boast made by electronic engineers that there is no such thing as an *electronic* failure—they are all mechanical failures.

PLATE 1.1. A Vulcan flies across desert terrain inappropriately camouflaged. Even if the camouflage was changed, the large black shadow would be the perfect give-away. This shot clearly shows the shadow of the Jet Provost photographic chase aircraft showing that ground shadow can give information on the range of the attacking aircraft if the conditions are right. (Crown copyright.)

PLATE 2.1. Harrier GR3, the RAF close support version of the unique vectored thrust design. The elongated nose containing the Laser Marked Target Seeker, combined with the large 'elephant ear' intakes and the bulbous fuselage housing the impressive Pegasus engine makes even its most ardent supporters concede that it is not a thing of beauty—but highly effective nevertheless. Harriers can, and do, operate away from main bases for lengthy periods and this capability has attracted the USMC to the aircraft. Their developed version, the AV-8B, will also be purchased for the RAF. Four No. 4 Squadron aircraft are seen here, flying in non-tactical formation, over Germany. (Crown copyright.)

PLATE 2.2. An F-4 Phantom showing the high fire power of modern air defence aircraft. Four Aim 9 Sidewinder missiles are fitted to the inner pylons and four Skyflash or Sparrow missiles fitted conformally under the fuselage. RAF F-4s do not have an internal gun but a gun pod can be fitted instead of the fuel tank shown here on the centre line. Internal guns are fitted to nearly all modern generation fighters. Also shown is the degree of shielding of the jet pipes by the tailplane from top aspects.

PLATE 2.3. The F-16C, one of the most popular of the new generation fighter aircraft and one which has already made a successful transition to the attack role. Clearly seen here is the bubble canopy affording excellent view to the pilot over the full 360 degrees—even the canopy arch has been dispensed with. The F-16 is capable of a sustained 9*g* at the lower altitudes and reclined seating, side stick allowing support to the arms, and the capability to operate all the main combat functions from the stick and the throttle have been built in to the design to help the pilot cope with the forces involved. Even then, few pilots can withstand 9*g* for more than a short time—but time enough to gain a kill. (General Dynamics.)

PLATE 2.4. The A-10 Thunderbolt II ground attack aircraft of the USAF. This is the classic of its *genre*—armed with a GAU-8 Gatling cannon, heavily armoured, and slow, it relies on brute force rather than finesse to achieve its aim. Yet another less than attractive aircraft it is known, affectionately, as the 'Warthog'.

PLATE 2.5. The size of the Soviet MiG-21 compared to that of the US F-5.

PLATE 2.6. The F-5 flying alongside the F-15 showing how much easier the larger aircraft is to see. Fortunately Soviet design practice seems to be following that of the West and larger designs are becoming the norm. (Author.)

3

Tactics

This volume is concerned with air-to-ground operations and it would be inappropriate to delve too deeply into the subject of air combat tactics. However, as the penetrating offensive aircraft will be hunted by air defence fighters, and as the purpose of 'fighter-bombers' is to be able to fight their way into and out of the target area, the subject cannot be ignored.

A popular perception of air tactics is of some aerial game of chess; a stylised ballet danced to a set of given rules and moves. There are similarities. It is as necessary to plan ahead in combat as it is in chess, even though in combat the planning ahead may involve only a few seconds; both 'games' require continuous practice if success is to be ensured. But there the analogy wears thin. In chess the quantity and quality of the pieces on both sides are the same; in air combat that is rarely so. Chess is played to man-made rules; air combat is governed more by the rules of physics than of man. Indeed, where man can deceive and cheat, so more surely will success be achieved. It is not by accident that the favoured direction for attack is from the low 6 o'clock where the attacker can remain unseen. The odd tale of chivalry in the air must not be taken out of perspective, for air combat is one of the few military arts where surrender is not an option, quarter can rarely be requested or granted, and 'hard school' rules have to be the order of the day.

Because aircraft have different characteristics, it is important to know the advantages and disadvantages of the various types likely to be encountered. The scaling of aircraft from photographs and the subsequent analysis of likely performance is a specialist and well-developed art which enables the diligent combat pilot to enter battle with a fair assessment of his opponent's performance. The task thereafter is to ensure that the fight is conducted under the conditions of maximum disadvantage to the enemy. To know where this area is, performance is generally examined in three areas.

Specific Excess Power (SEP) is the measure of the power available, under any given flight condition, for changing the state of the aircraft. It is a measure of the excess power available after the drag of the aircraft has been overcome by thrust. Consequently, when an aircraft is flying at full throttle and going as fast as it can its SEP is zero; all of the available power is being used to counteract drag. If an aircraft is at its maximum ceiling, its SEP is zero. The only way it could climb further would be to zoom climb, but this would cause a loss of speed; that is, the energy would come from this source. At the top of the zoom the SEP would be a negative value, indicating that the aircraft could not be sustained at that state and it would have to descend to the point where SEP was again at zero. SEP is a good broad comparative measure of performance between two aircraft. If at 400 kts at

10,000 ft, for example, one aircraft had an SEP of 200 and another 250, then the latter would be *potentially* superior.

Air combat in the past had tended to be a manoeuvring engagement, and the ability of an aircraft to turn is an important measure of potential. *Sustained Turn Rate* (STR) is the quality which studies show to be the most important measure of air combat potential. Expressed in degrees per second (°/sec), it is the ability of the aircraft to turn at that rate continuously. The ability of the aircraft to do this is dependent upon having enough thrust to balance the drag in the turn while maintaining speed; therefore, the STR of an aircraft is dependent upon *thrust*. An aircraft showing a high SEP at a given flight condition, therefore, might be suspected of having good STR, providing that handling or aerodynamic characteristics were reasonably well matched. Good STR is important in situations where weapon capability and similar performance profiles give rise to stalemate situations or those where advantage is gained or lost slowly. Air combat simulations have shown that a STR advantage of 2 °/sec can be a dominating factor in an engagement; a difference of 5 °/sec gives results equivalent to those where there is a 2–1 numerical advantage.

Attained Turn Rate (ATR) is another turn characteristic of importance, and is the maximum turn rate which can be attained. It is governed by the amount of *lift* available, or by the structural limitation on the airframe, and is not a steady-state condition. It is normally used for short periods; for example, to break the lock of a missile, to spoil an enemy's gun solution or, offensively, to pull the nose onto an opponent for either a snap gun shot or to enable missile heads to acquire. The penalty is loss of speed, or height, or both, and the tactic has to be used with care. At the end of the manoeuvre the aircraft can be left in a low-energy state, and therefore more vulnerable to re-attack or to attack by enemy wingmen.

It is this consideration which causes the sometimes inflated claims made for 'VIFF-ing' or the vectoring-of-thrust-in-flight used by the Harrier, to be treated with some caution. In a one-on-one engagement, where the VIFF-ing, or the enhanced maximum attained turn, is used in defence or offence, it is usually possible to judge fairly accurately whether the lower energy state can be safely accepted. In a multi-aircraft interaction, where it is difficult to keep a mental plot of the whole fight, it is unwise, even dangerous, to kill energy. The manoeuvre may succeed against one opponent but leave an easy shot for another. Analysis over the years has shown that as many as 80 per cent of aircraft shot down in combat have fallen to aircraft which have not been seen. One analysis of gun camera film showed that over 70 per cent of aircraft being engaged during a conflict had less than 30° of bank applied when hit. This accounts in some part for the success obtained by large numbers of simple aircraft in engagements against lesser numbers of much more sophisticated aircraft. Theoretically there should be little contest, but practically the small, *unseen* aircraft obtains the kill against technological odds. It forms a part of the argument which continues to rage about numbers versus technology; quantity versus quality. It will continue for some time yet; there is no simple answer, and the discussion is regularly clouded by the scenario selected. Only one thing is sure; a *few, simple* aircraft will not suffice.

Of the three main parameters, therefore, it can be seen that two, SEP and STR, are mainly thrust-dependent, and ATR is lift-dependent.

It is also necessary to the discussion of air combat to be aware of the relationships between four parameters, largely interconnected, which govern the geometry of the engagement: *speed, g, radius of turn* and *rate of turn.* An understanding of these factors and their relationship can be had by study of some simple equations.

Radius of turn (in ft) and rate of turn (in °/sec—ω) are two important combat parameters, and it is necessary to avoid the pitfall of assuming that minimum radius is the same condition as maximum rate, or vice versa. In different combat situations there is a need to use either minimum radius or maximum rate, and mistaking the conditions for either could lead to unfortunate results.

$$\text{Radius of turn } (R) = \frac{v^2}{g}.$$

The point to note from the formula for radius of turn is that *at equal speeds* the aircraft which can pull the greatest g out-turns the other. More important is that the v factor is a squared function. At a given g, therefore, a doubling of the speed gives a quadrupling of the turn radius. A popular misconception is that it is aircraft design which governs this relationship. It does so only in that the aircraft must be able to achieve the speed and produce enough lift to pull the g, but thereafter the relationship is purely one of physics. The same relationship exists for any body moving in a similar fashion. It is physics not aerodynamics.

It is necessary to refer to the aircraft's performance diagram, plotting the turn rate available against speed, known sometimes as the 'doghouse' diagram because of its similar shape. This plot illustrates the characteristics of the aircraft and is an important source of information for comparison with other aircraft. An example

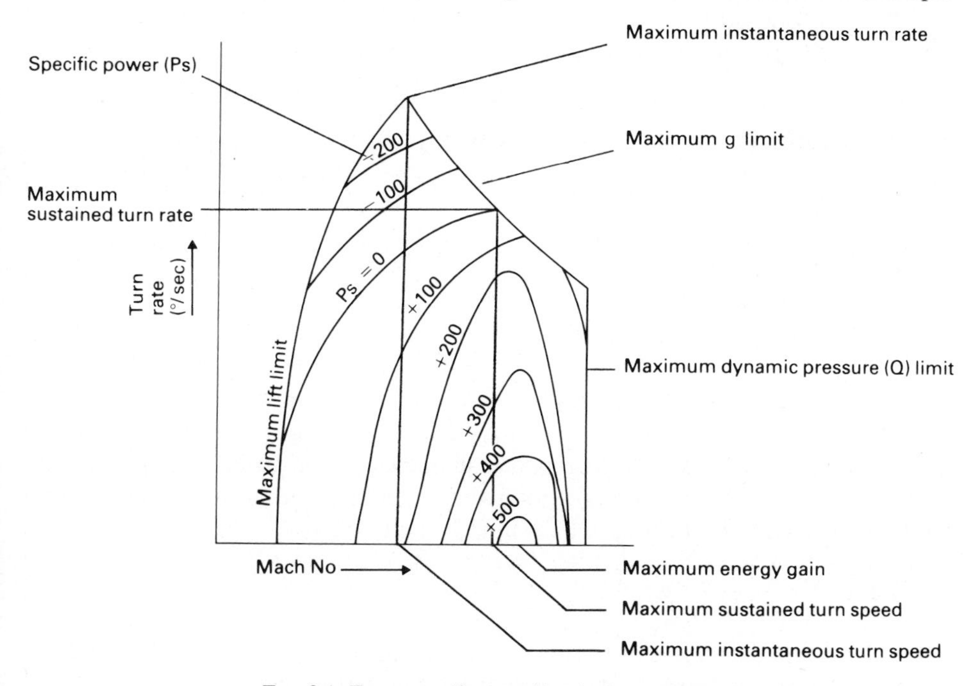

FIG. 3.1. Turn rate diagram (the doghouse plot).

of such a plot is seen at Fig. 3.1, and shows the speed at which the turn rate on the vertical axis can be sustained. The characteristic shape is caused by the need to capitalise on the speed to produce lift, which in turn generates *g*. Past the peak, the fall-off is caused by a variety of factors. The onset of compressibility can reduce the lift generated by some wings, or the amount of power available is insufficient to both produce the increased speed and overcome the lift-induced drag caused by pulling *g*. It can be also arbitrarily modified in this area by the structural limit of the aircraft. Typically, a modern combat aircraft built with agility in mind may have a maximum rate of turn around the 300–400 kt area. Rates of turn at low level in the order of 20 °/sec are not uncommon.

The formulae for radius of turn is:

$$\text{w °/sec} = \frac{180 \cdot v}{\pi R}$$

Together with the formulae for radius of turn, the relevant formulae for speed, *g*, radius and rate of turn can be derived.

PERFORMANCE EQUATIONS

Specific power (P_s)

$$P_s = \frac{V(T-D)}{W}$$

where V=velocity (ft/sec),
T=thrust (lb),
D=drag (lb),
W=weight,
P_s=0 when thrust=drag.

There are five factors affecting the study of a horizontal turn:

v=aircraft time air speed (TAS) (ft/sec),
R=turn radius (ft),
g=force of gravity (32.17 ft/sec^2),
w=rate of turn (radians/sec),
n=g indicated in the cockpit,
a=angle of bank (degrees).

These factors are related thus:

$$Vw = \frac{v^2}{R} = g \tan a = g\sqrt{(n^2-1)}.$$

The radius of turn in the vertical plane is affected by the differential effect of *g* when upright at the bottom of a loop and when inverted at the top of a loop. Where y=angle of climb/dive (0°=upright level flight)

$$\text{Radius} = \frac{1}{(n-\cos y)}\,\frac{V}{g}.$$

By calculating the radius at bottom, vertical and inverted points of a constant speed loop, it can be seen that the shape resembles an egg.

A half-day's amusement with the performance equations and a pocket calculator returns a handsome dividend in the understanding of the fundamentals of air combat. It will show that to break a missile lock, or to force an overshoot by a fast approaching enemy, a minimum radius turn is required. By reference to the best speed for minimum radius from the V–N diagram a pilot can preplan this emergency manoeuvre. It may be initiated from high speed and will first require a pull to the maximum structural limit, to hold this until the speed decays to the point where the *g* starts falling through the maximum, and to check when the speed falls further to the point where minimum radius speed is attained, three quite distinct 'steps' (Fig. 3.2). Further, it may pay in high-performance aircraft to throttle back initially to lose speed as quickly as possible, and to add power as the minimum radius speed is approached to sustain it. As the natural inclination amongst many pilots is to go to maximum power as combat is engaged, a habit engrained from the days when aircraft were more power-limited than today, this can be a difficult lesson to learn. Against an IR missile attack two further advantages result; by throttling back, the level of IR emission is reduced, and in some aircraft, the F-4 and Jaguar, for example, the hot jet pipes can be obscured by the tailplane in the turn. Equally, if the aim is to change direction over a large angle, a maximum STR turn may be required. An example of such a requirement could be when a target has passed rapidly on a reciprocal heading and a turn is required to bring missile heads to bear. Until relatively recently, such a pass would have left the target invulnerable. By the time the fighter had turned, the target would have been well out of range. The advent of the new agile fighters has changed this, and turn rates in the order of 20 °/sec and missiles with long range and off-boresight capability can mean a successful engagement even under these demanding conditions. With a 40° off-boresight missile, for example, a 450-kt target aircraft could have missile heads acquiring while still only about a mile from the fighter, well within the normal envelope of a modern air-to-air missile (Fig. 3.5).

Such performance brings about a rare step change to the air combat scene. In the past it has been possible to disengage from a combat by engineering a head-on pass and flying out of the fight. Now that this escape manoeuvre is no longer necessarily effective, the spectre arises of the truly gladiatorial battle, one in which, once engaged, only the victor emerges. That victory need not necessarily go to the best pilot, or even to the best equipment, but may go to the side who can stay engaged longest. He who runs first may die first, and the fuel gauge assumes a new and vital importance, for the fuel fraction, and consumption rates under combat power, determines the ability to stay engaged. *Persistence* is becoming a term increasingly used in the discussion of air combat.

The determination of SEP, STR, ATR and the understanding of the inter-relationship of speed, *g*, radius and rate of turn will give a sound basis for some theoretical understanding of the combat scene. For a practical understanding allowance must be made for a host of other factors, many of which defy quantification.

The importance in combat of being able to 'see' the enemy first is considerable. 'Seeing' in this case can mean equally seeing by visual or radar means or by other sensors. The design of the cockpit can influence the ability to visually acquire

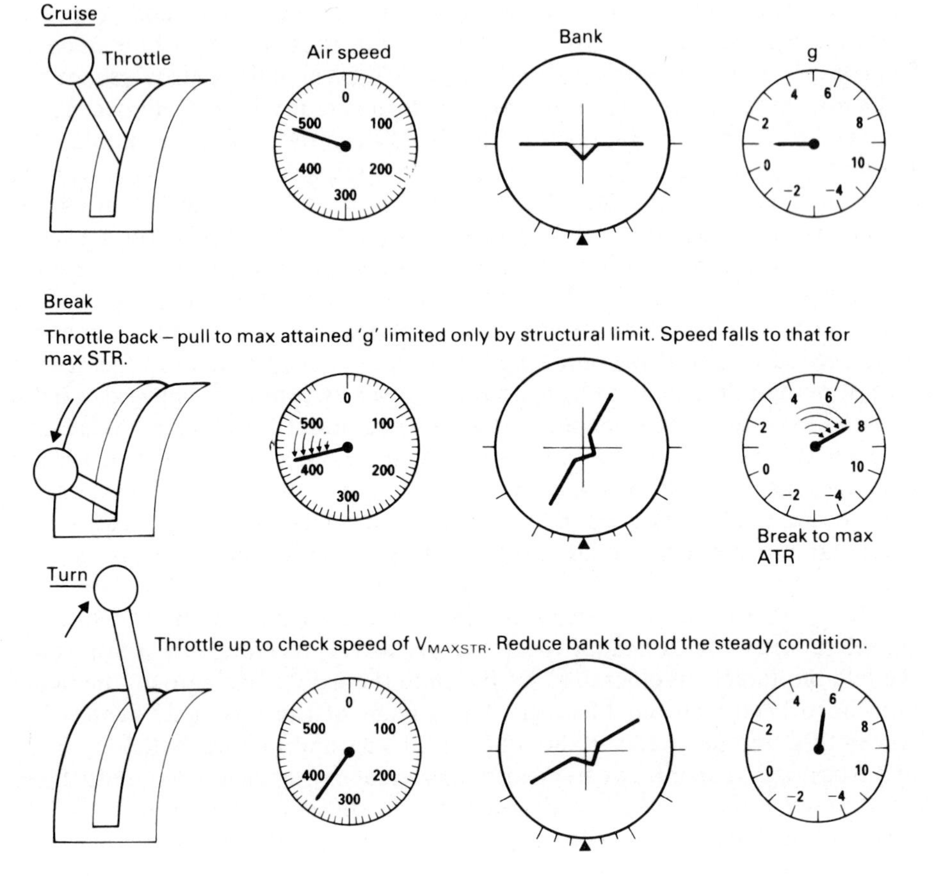

FIG. 3.2. The flying of a break against an attack sighted late.

other aircraft and a comparison between the MiG-21 and the F-16 will show the importance placed upon field of view in the new agile fighters compared to those of some years ago. It is an area where pilot insistence has triumphed over the designer's natural reluctance to place obtrusive canopies on the upper surfaces of their designs. In some instances, the turbulence inspired by bubble canopies, particularly at high angles of attack, can severely affect the airflow over a single in-line fin and rudder and can be one of the factors driving designers into twin fins as in the F-14, F-15 and F-18. There has also been a move towards the reduction, or even elimination, of the cockpit arches or supports to remove obstructions to the field of view; the F-16 shows this in practice. Considerable demands are placed upon one-piece transparent structures which not only have to be able to withstand high air pressures and impact damage from birdstrike, but must also possess excellent optical qualities.

Having achieved the agile aircraft with its bubble canopy permitting a much improved rear view, there is the problem of capitalising on the performance while restricted to a mortal pilot. Modern agile aircraft can pull up to 9*g* and there is the

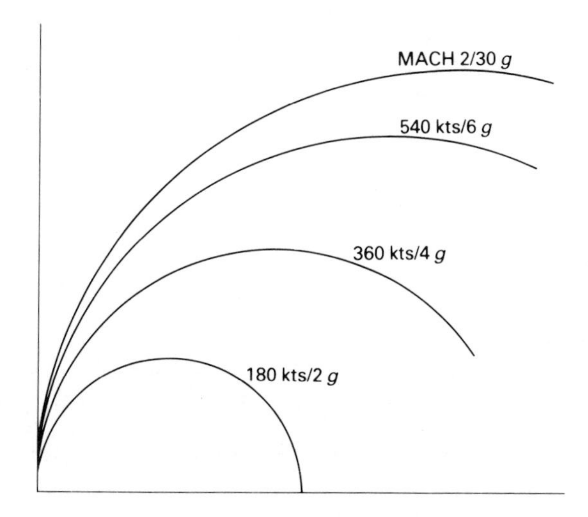

FIG. 3.3. Radii of turn at varying speed and *g*.

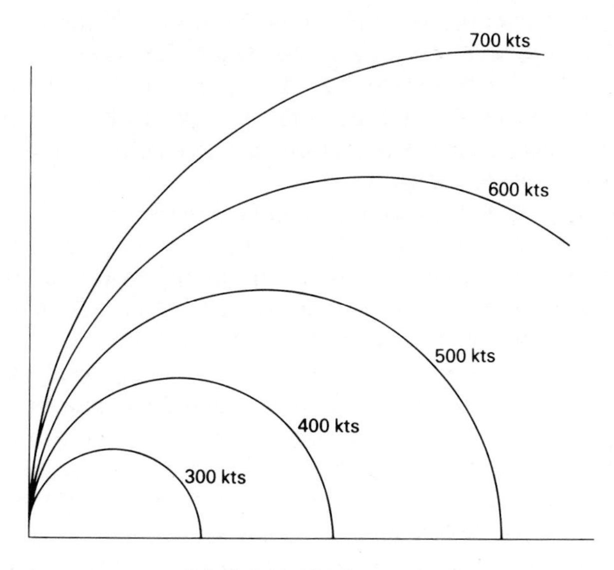

FIG. 3.4. Radii of turn at 6*g*.

problem of staying conscious at these high *g* levels, let alone looking to the rear at the same time. A compromise is required. To help withstand the *g*, seats have been reclined to lessen the 'head' of blood which has to be supported; legs have been raised as high as is practicable to avoid the blood 'pooling' in the lower limbs; side sticks instead of the normal centrally located configuration have enabled arms to be supported on rests. Together with good anti-*g* suits, these measures are

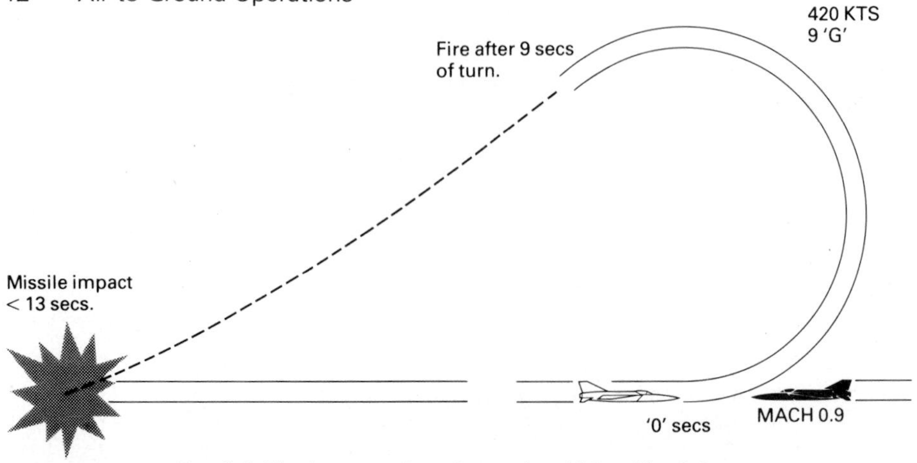

FIG. 3.5. The 'no escape' combat against high-agility fighters.

estimated to improve g tolerance by some 1.5 to 2:0g above more conventional arrangements. Problems still remain. The human being was built to turn his head rearward from the upright position, and the more the body is reclined, so the more difficult it is to look rearwards. A simple demonstration at home can be performed in an upright chair and on a reclining or easy chair. The strain on the neck when reclined and under high g levels can be a problem to pilots and medical officers alike. One air force recently estimated that a tour on the new high-g fighters resulted in pilots taking one size larger in shirt collars as a result of the development of the neck muscles.

Two pairs of eyes are better than one, and is a theme of the advocates of two-place aircraft. They must be right. But to increase the size of an aircraft to accommodate a second seat, and to commit to the increased training and career structure necessary to support a two-man rather than a single-man crew, makes this an expensive option and one which should be followed only if the second man is essential rather than desirable. If it is determined that a second man is required, as in the F-4 or the Tornado, it could be considered whether he should not be seated facing backwards. It would hardly affect system operation, but would greatly enhance the all-round surveillance of the crew as a whole. Rear gunners are still on the scene in the Soviet TU-95 Bear and in World War II the Boulton-Paul Defiant fighter had a rear-facing gunner, as did the Stuka.

The necessity for a two-man crew is not based primarily on the surveillance case, but more on the demands of cockpit workload. This can have an adverse effect on combat capability if it is high. Great strides have been made over the years to improve the cockpit environment and to automate functions. Where this is not done well, performance can be severely handicapped; pilots failing to release weapons because of switch positioning errors, regretfully, still occurs. Recently a fighter making a practice interception on a friendly aircraft inadvertently fired a live missile which destroyed the target. In the trauma of a real conflict, when fear and tension are present, cockpits which are, as some have been described, 'ergonomic slums' and demand complex drills and procedures, will cost effectiveness, missed targets, lost kills and unnecessary accidents. It is a factor worth taking into account.

Closely associated with cockpit ergonomics in the modern age is the performance of head-up displays (HUD). This equipment provides both the sighting information needed to deliver weapons, as did gun and bomb sights in the past, but also displays the essential flying information such as airspeed, altitude, vertical speed, heading and angle of attack. Some HUDs present a processed picture from the radar and show the pilot where to look to visually acquire a target. Navigation information can be displayed giving the pilot steering information to navigational waypoints stored in the computer. HUDs allow the pilot to keep his head 'out of the cockpit' and have been one of the more beneficial advances in the air combat and ground-attack field over the last few years, allowing target acquisition ranges to be improved. In the first HUDs the field of view was limited, and this in turn restricted the movement of the head. Improvements have been made recently, and now fields of view are commendably wide. Nonetheless, there is a finite limit to how wide the field of view on any HUD can be, and as radar gimbal limits are increased, missile head off-bore-sight capability is improved, and aircraft increasingly are fitted with all-round threat warning systems, there is a need for the pilot to be able ideally to see HUD information, particularly weapon systems information, over the whole range of azimuth and elevation he can physically cover. The answer to this is the helmet-mounted display which presents information to the pilot's eye through small helmet-mounted viewing screens.

The amount of information needing to be assimilated is increasing as radar spreads further from the air intercept role in the fighters to its use for terrain clearance and ground mapping in offensive aircraft. As the move towards 24-hr operations gains pace, so more offensive aircraft will be fitted with Forward Looking Infra-Red (FLIR) devices. In an attempt to increase acquisition range in the absence of reliable Identification Friend or Foe (IFF), some aircraft have fitted a cockpit telescope which can be laid on to a target by bore-sighting the radar. The effect of all these various information improvements is to increase the amount of data the pilot or crew must absorb. The cockpit and system design which best assists in this task could play a large part in the success or failure of a mission.

The air-to-air missile for some time has been the primary air-to-air weapon. Operationally its success has been less than expected, and analysis has shown that a reason for its disappointing showing was that many were fired outside their effective envelopes. This was particularly true in Vietnam. The effective envelope of an air-to-air missile is a complex shape, normally resembling a kidney with a double indentation. The shapes depicted in manuals are good for only the conditions specified, and any change in target speed or emission characteristics, particularly in the case of infrared missiles, can change the shape of the envelope appreciably. To assess whether or not the missile is within its engagement parameters during the stress of combat is a demanding task and is the reason in the past for so many pilot-induced failures. Where information on target position is available, from a radar for example, and where that information can be processed and presented to the pilot as a FIRE/HOLD command, the effectiveness of the fighter can be substantially increased.

A good missile design can assist pilots of aircraft not radar equipped. Usually such aircraft are fitted with infrared missiles, and if the head is designed to lock on to a target only within the off-boresight and range capabilities of the missile itself, then the pilot can confidently fire once he receives indication of a missile head acquisition, normally a warning light or an audible 'growl'. Even then there are complications in a multi-aircraft engagement in deciding which aircraft has been acquired by the missile; to an infrared missile, friend can look remarkably similar to foe.

Although air combat is becoming more technical in the missile and electronic age, and comparisons of aircraft are made in mathematical and scientific terms rather than subjectively, the skill and experience of the pilot still counts for much. Of all the dictums of successful commanders in the past there can be none more applicable in air combat as Napoleon's: 'Do not underestimate the enemy.' It matters not whether the whole of the enemy air force is a shambles if the one pilot you happen to be fighting is the exception about which folk songs will be written. Equally, if fighting the finest squadron in the world their reputation means nought if you are at $\frac{1}{2}$ mile in the 6 o'clock. The prudent combat pilot always enters a combat conceding the fact that he is engaging the world's second greatest fighter pilot—any fighter pilot worth his salt know that he is the world's first! Such caution, tempered only by modesty, can avoid the pitfall of judging the quality of an air force by, amongst other things, the number of hours flown. This can be deceptive unless the whole training picture is considered. Take an air force whose pilots fly 80 hr per year compared with one doing 160 hr per year. Theoretically one should be twice as well trained as the other. But not necessarily so. If one has to fly 20 mins there and back to a range to conduct a 20-min range sortie, the penalty is 1 hr flying. If the other air force have their range facilities very close to their base, and some have such facilities almost within the traffic pattern, then the same amount of training can be accomplished for half of the flying time. One air force may fly so-called 'multi-role' aircraft and have to allocate their larger number of hours over two or three roles. The other air force may concentrate their fewer hours on one specialist role. As it will be in this role that the interaction is made, the air force which on paper flies less hours may be the better trained.

The message is, therefore, that there is more to an air force than sheer numbers and more to air combat potential than the obvious parameters. Put together, the many factors almost defy any meaningful comparison and the proof of superiority may have to await day one of the conflict.

In applying this background to ground attack operations, the comparisons made above have to be tempered with an even more important constraint. The air defence fighter will be operating in a more optimised manner than the fighter-bomber penetrator. The fighter will be operating over his own territory with friendly bases available for diversion in the event of fuel shortage or elongated pursuit. He can therefore fight to lower fuel states than can the penetrator, who has to make his target and return home. The greatest weight difference is, however, that of the armament. The air defence fighter may have air-to-air missiles which generally are relatively small and light, while the penetrator may be encumbered by heavier and bulkier attack weapons and drop tanks. Although 'drop' tanks are supposed to be dropped if the occasion demands, pilots will be reluctant to do so if there is still fuel in them or if they are scarce. This latter reason may sound strange, but the modern drop tank can be a complex and expensive item and is seldom stocked in such profusion that they can be jettisoned on operational missions without due consideration. The effect of a wing exhausting their stock of drop tanks is to reduce the number of the targets it can attack through lack of reach. If a defensive force can cause penetrators to jettison their scarce drop tanks early in a conflict, those targets between the clean and tanked range of the penetrating force will have been perfectly defended without a shot being fired. A most cost-effective defence.

Both drop tanks and ground-attack weapons, particularly bombs, have large frontal areas and, together with their suspension equipment, pylons and release units, can add considerably to the total drag of the aircraft. Some combinations of tanks and bombs can double the drag of an aircraft, with consequent effects on fuel consumption and maximum speed. The designer is always searching for means of reducing this drag penalty. The best method is to carry the weapons internally in a bomb bay. The Buccaneer is an example of this in practice, and the advantages gained in both penetration speed and range makes this elderly design a potent weapon even today. On new designs, weapons can be made to fit flush, or semi-buried, to the airframe, so reducing their effective frontal area and the interference drag caused by airflow passing over two bodies in close proximity. The semi-buried carriage of air-to-air weapons on the F-4 and the Tornado F-2 illustrates this well. The method does have its disadvantages. It is sometimes necessary to optimise the weapon carriage to a restricted range of weapons, so limiting flexibility. Where there is widespread standardisation of weapons, as in the Warsaw Pact forces, the disadvantage is small. Another method of reducing the drag of external stores is to mount them in tandem, one behind another. This shows a useful drag reduction over arrangements which mount the weapons laterally.

The effect of the drag and weight of external weapons cannot be over-emphasised. Compared with the clean aircraft, radius of action can be reduced by around a half; nominally supersonic aircraft can be limited to maximum speeds in dry power in the upper 400- or lower 500-knot range; an aircraft which could pull 7*g* when 'clean' may have difficulty sustaining much over 3*g* when loaded with stores. Clearly the ground-attack pilot, labouring under such disadvantages is unlikely to outmanoeuvre the interceptor even if he is the better pilot.

The extent to which pilot skill can offset performance disadvantage is a favourite subject for debate. It can also be used unfortunately to excuse some performance or training deficiency. It is probably impossible to match performance with the more subjective assessment of pilot ability, but if the opponent has a 2 or more *g* advantage and a 100–150 knot overtake capability it would be asking a great deal of any pilot to offset such a margin by skill alone. Most interceptors could be assumed to have such a margin when attacking heavily-laden penetrating aircraft.

Accepting that performance parity is probably unobtainable, the offensive pilot must look to other ways of achieving his mission objectives. The most obvious is to remain unseen. Visually this means remaining as small as possible, and employing to the full the advances made in camouflage over the years. There are many variations of camouflage patterns, and each have their advocates, but all must be attuned to the environment in which the aircraft will be used. A desert camouflage would not be ideal for the dull greens and browns of Central Europe or vice versa. Self-help and initiative must not be ruled out; a layer of snow over the full greens and browns can be allowed for by the application of some white distemper at squadron level to give an effective 'winter' camouflage. Come the thaw, hot water and detergent restores the approved pattern. In dull weather, or when flying in the shadow of clouds, most camouflage schemes in use in Europe are very effective, but when flying in bright sunlight the shadow cast by the aircraft travelling across the ground can be the first indication to the interceptor. This shadow is much less marked when flying over wooded terrain, and it might be worth planning the sortie to exploit such opportunities if there is a high chance of visual interception.

A great boon to interceptors searching for visual acquisitions is engine smoke trail. Great attention is now being paid to reducing smoke emission from military engines, and following their experience in Vietnam smoke-free engines have been specified by the USAF. In the past there have been some bad examples of smokey engines. The otherwise excellent engine in F-104, F-105 and F-4, the J79, was notorious in this respect. The problem is worse when looking along the engine exhaust from head-on or tail-on. A bad engine can present a dark smudge visible for many miles, particularly in clear air. Looking across the slipstream presents less of a problem even with poor engines.

The opportunity to detect an aircraft, or its smoke signature, is increased if the target can be 'sky-lined', or seen against the clear sky background rather than against the earth backdrop. To do this the interceptor attempting a visual acquisition must fly low, ideally as low, if not lower, than the target aircraft. This can be a very demanding task if the target aircraft is penetrating at a sensibly low height, because if the interceptor pilot is going to concentrate sufficiently on his search, the attention spent on ground avoidance will be reduced to his potential embarrassment. Further, if he flies low to enhance his visual acquisition chances, he will jeopardise his radar acquisition if he flies low enough for ground returns to affect his picture. A better tactic, if it can be arranged, is to position the combat air patrol on the far side of some ridge feature which the target aircraft will have to traverse. If the target stays low as he approaches the ridge, he will tend to be 'thrown' high, because he is unable to push sufficient negative *g*.

Conversely, the ground-attack pilot must develop techniques to enable him to stay as low as possible as he crosses ridge lines. Two methods are popular. The first entails 'ironing out' the ridge by flying so as to be able to pass the peak of the ridge in level flight or even anticipating the downward path required on the lee side. While this prevents any excessive gain of height, it nonetheless accepts a height gain over the ideal on both sides of the ridge, and during these periods the penetrating aircraft is not only vulnerable to skylining but also to engagement by ground-based defensive systems.

The second method is by far the best. The ridge feature is approached at an angle and maintaining low altitude while flying up the approach side. As the top is approached, the aircraft is rolled inverted and the contour of the ridge is maintained by then pulling *g*. As the lee side is reached, the aircraft is returned to conventional flight and, still at low level, turned onto the desired heading (Fig.

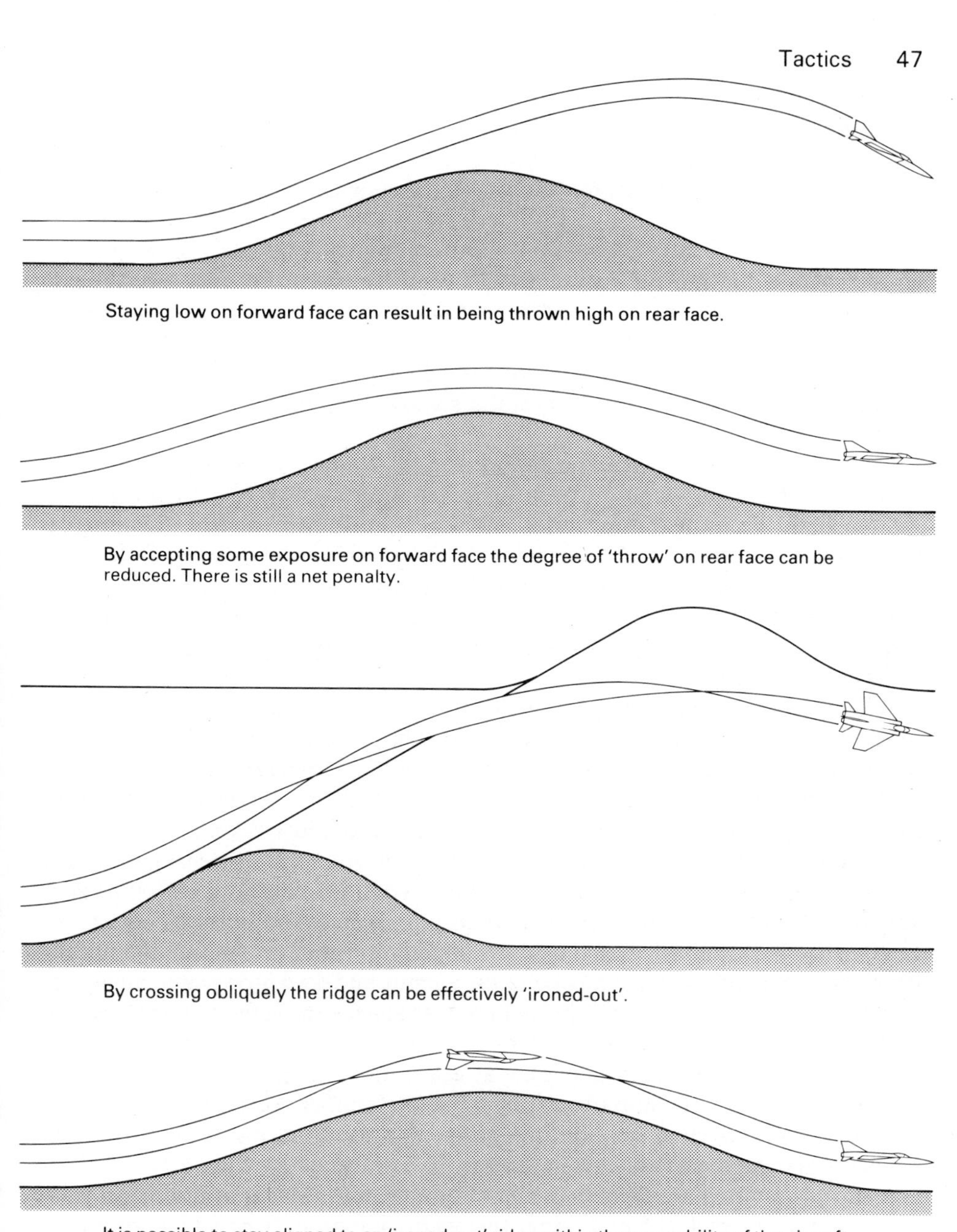

FIG. 3.6. Ridge crossing.

3.6). Although the manoeuvre is perfectly safe and highly controllable from the pilot's point of view, the prospect of being upside down only a few feet from the ground requires trusting crew members.

Routing is highly important to the avoidance of visual detection. Valleys can be exploited to prevent skylining, and can make the interceptor's task most difficult, particularly if a gun attack is being made. In this case the tight valley sides can constrain the interceptor's attack pattern and a meandering valley can result in an elusive target.

It is not only visual detection which has to be considered. It is possible to detect a variety of electronic emissions from aircraft varying from radio transmissions to intercept radars, terrain-following or ground-mapping radars and even radar altimeter transmissions. In future, such equipment cannot be used thoughtlessly or needlessly, and if a mission can be completed satisfactorily in a purely passive manner, then it will be prudent to do so. Passive warning receiver (PWR) devices, designed to detect certain transmissions and display to the pilot the direction from which they are emanating, will become standard equipment in aircraft in the future.

In the radar battle they can be potent devices. Radar works on the basis of an energy transmission which impacts the target and reflects sufficient energy to be received by the transmitting source. Clearly, therefore, a transmission can normally be received by a PWR at a greater distance than the emitter can receive a reflection. The PWR-equipped aircraft will generally get an indication of being hunted before the hunter obtains a detection. Used intelligently, this can greatly assist the penetrating aircraft to locate, and to avoid, combat air patrols if they are using their intercept radars.

Where radars have to be used, at night or in poor weather, they should be used as little as possible. Allied to good reliable navigation systems, a single, or very few, radar points where the picture can be memorised by the system can prove sufficient for most navigation *en route.* Where the radar is being used for terrain-following, few crews would be satisfied with anything short of the maximum data rate. Obviously designers attempt to make such radars secure against jamming or intercept; beams are made as narrow as possible, side lobes are reduced by good antennae design or by suppression, and both frequency and pulse repetition rate can be changed regularly to make intercept and interpretation more difficult. But the electronic revolution equally helps the enemy, and data processing can be used to solve some of the problems presented. It is always the safer course to assume that if a transmission is made, equally a detection could be made.

An additional constraint facing the attack pilot seeking to achieve the covert approach falls from the absence of any reliable identification (IFF) system. Until this long-standing and debilitating problem is solved, resort to procedural airspace management systems is bound to continue. Having to abide by a procedural system may remove routing choice from the leader's options, and may determine where he has first to enter the enemy airspace. If, or when, the enemy determines the procedural 'rules', his fighter force can be concentrated to await the penetrating formations. This is just one of the many grave disadvantages which can fall from not having a reliable IFF system; there are others from both fighter and missile viewpoints. The IFF requirement must feature high on the list of any air commander's investment priorities; its all-pervading effect gives it a strong case for preferential investment. One senior NATO air commander estimates that a reliable IFF system would increase the overall effectiveness of his force by 25 per cent; he was criticised only by those who thought him too conservative.

Both formation leader and tasking authority alike must understand the nuances of the principle of war—*concentration of force.* Because Clausewitz, the great writer on war, suggested that the attacker required a three-to-one advantage over the defender to achieve his purpose, and land commanders have generally concurred with this through the years, there is a tendency to believe that it is a universal truth equally applicable to all the forms of warfare. It is not disrespectful to the great man, who wrote with land warfare in nineteenth-century Europe in mind, to suggest that in both naval and air warfare this is not necessarily so. The number of frigates required to protect a convoy from a single submarine, or the air defence fighters required to defend against a threat, suggests that while the numerical ratio may be debatable, the defender is nowhere near so favourably placed as he is in the land battle environment. At the end of World War I, one German source claimed that 400 fighters were being used to counter the threat from a force of only 40 bombers, and the defensive resources in terms of aircraft, escorts and submarines used to protect the US carriers are indeed remarkable.

The reason for this change in emphasis between the three operational environments, land, sea and air, is based on the ability of the attacker to achieve surprise, to choose his time to attack and to concentrate. Airmen frequently talk of the *flexibility* of air power which encompasses these qualities, but care needs to be taken that in so doing the attributes of each are not lost. How Clausewitz's ratio changes might, on reflection, be thought to have something to do with the *speed* which action takes place in the three mediums. The *One-Five Rule* can be applied: a land battle occurs at rates of advance of 1.5 kts; a naval force may transit at 15 kts; an air battle may involve closures of 1,500 kts. The difficulty of achieving surprise at land speeds is more difficult than at air speeds. More time is required to concentrate at land speeds than at air speeds. The rate at which things happen largely governs 'surprise' and it follows that surprise in the age of near-real-time surveillance can be achieved best by air power.

The defender must be prepared to defend at all points at all times if he is not to accept some targets undefended. This is a demanding task, which can soon exhaust resources unless they are tightly controlled. That is true of virtually all air defence situations, but solutions are highly dependent upon the geography of both defence and offence.

In time, the defender has a 24-hr task. Even in World War I, there were night operations, and in World War II the bulk of Bomber Command's efforts were at night. With the advent of Terrain Following Radar and night-vision devices, night operations will become more the norm in the future, and this will place great demands on the defenders. Twenty-four-hour operations are very wearing of men and material, and the advantages are real to those allowed by geography to stand alert on the ground rather than in the air. Because of the high cost of aircrew, most Western air forces man their squadrons to tight aircrew-to-aircraft ratios. These ratios are rarely much above 1.5:1 in the fast-jet combat squadrons. The complexity of modern aircraft and the costs of staying current, or the time involved in retraining, both conspire to prevent major reinforcement of the front line in an emergency. Consequently, the war will have to be fought largely with the peacetime complement. Clearly, if the attacker can by operations or subterfuge ensure that the defender is forced to operate continuously, he can reasonably expect the *strain* soon to tell.

Geography, and the possession of the all-important range to exploit it, is a most important factor. If the defender's bases are well to the rear, the attacker may be able to penetrate to shallow targets and withdraw well before the defenders can react. This may force them into CAP operations or to rely on missile defence for the immediate frontal area. As this is an area of confused airspace control, with a profusion of land weapons involved, there is some merit in this approach. But when defenders are on ground alert, substantial penetrations can be made before an intercept is possible unless a measure of early warning is available. It is this which makes the Airborne Warning and Control System (AWACS) such an important factor on the battlefield, if its early warning can mean the difference between ground alert and CAP, it becomes a 'force multiplier' of a major kind. Its control function also makes the fighters more effective once they are airborne.

The offensive answer to the defensive posture is saturation attack (Fig. 3.7). This can be applied in two main areas: the first is over the target where the point defences can be swamped by saturation attack; the second is in the penetration of the highly defended forward area where ground forces point defence systems are added to the area air defence threat. By presenting the attacking aircraft singly, or in small packages, the task of the defensive forces is eased considerably. Penetrating in larger numbers not only increases the confusion in the air defence picture but also gives rise to a synergistic effect from the various counter-measures carried by the penetrators. One aircraft's ECM pod can defend another aircraft in close proximity.

Not all targets will warrant the expenditure of sufficient effort to obtain a saturation of the forward area defences. In these cases the tasking authorities must arrange force 'packages' which will penetrate together for mutual support before separating beyond the intensive forward defences to proceed to their individual targets.

Another reason for force 'packaging' is the scarcity of the highly specialised penetration support or defence suppression forces. These forces include such assets as the USAF F-4G Wild Weasel force, escort jammers and stand-off jammers all designed to degrade anti-aircraft systems by either active or passive means.

This is a particular problem for the NATO forces because of the profusion and variety of Warsaw Pact systems. Whereas in the West a new system will tend to replace the older model, over the years the Soviets have tended to add new systems to the inventory, with the result that the defensive system density has increased, the gaps in cover have tended to be reduced or in many cases cover is now overlapped, and the problem of the counter-measure designer magnified by a great variety of frequencies and modes of operation. With such a profusion of differing systems the advantage of seeking the synergistic effect of force packages is more clear.

How many aircraft constitute a sufficiently large package to ensure saturation will depend on many factors, but it is an area where any doubt should be resolved by using more rather than less aircraft. Some packages are envisaged as being about 40 aircraft, others many more than 100 aircraft, but there can be no general

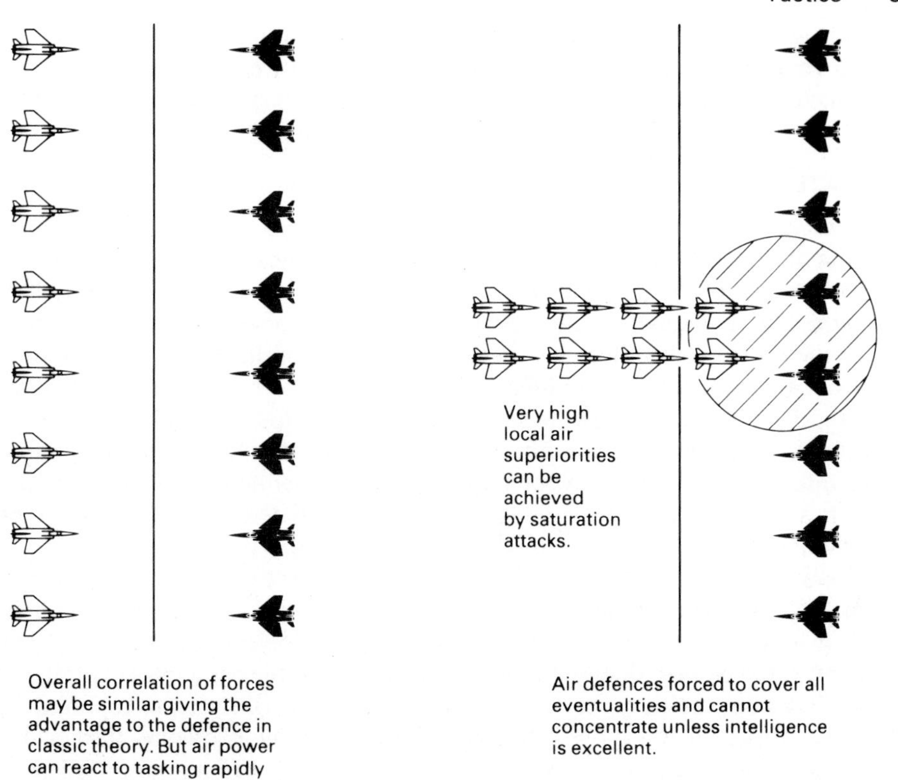

FIG. 3.7. Saturation.

rule and packages will have to be orchestrated in the light of circumstances existing at the time.

The inability to do any more than general preplanning presents its own problem. Such packages have to rendezvous, for the size required will generally be beyond the ability of any one base alone to field. Unlike the days in World War II when the bomber streams would take an hour or more to assemble, modern jet aircraft have insufficient fuel reserves to allow for such procedures. The package will have to form up *en route*, and this demands the most careful prebriefing, not only because the misidentification of a formation trying to enter the stream could result in it being engaged, but also because the package could well consist of formations from different nations, all with their own particular standard operating procedures and unique ways of looking at the task. As the identification of a 'mission leader' in these circumstances would be difficult, and his briefing requirements to fulfil such a role almost impossible to provide, the system must rely on good, sound, but simple rules which allow each crew to know what they should be doing, where and when. It sounds simple, but it is far from being so, yet the advantage to be gained from saturation is so great that the effort must be made to solve the difficulties.

In the *en route* phase the task of the attack formation is to first evade the defences and if necessary to suppress the defences. Before considering the problem of defence suppression, the basic tenets of formation flying are worthy of mention.

FORMATION TACTICS

The success achieved by the legendary Baron Manfred von Richtofen in the air combats of World War I was due in some measure to his early realisation of what have become since the self-evident truths; the advantages of attack from out of the sun, and the interrelationship between height and speed, but perhaps none contributed more to his success than the exploitation of the attack from the low 6 o'clock, leaving the target unsighted and unaware (Fig. 3.8). To this day the attack from the low rear is still one which presents problems, and although bomber aircraft have long been fitted with tail armament, as has the occasional fighter or attack aircraft, the Defiant and the Stuka for example, defence against the rear attack has long rested on the formation. The wingman defends the leader and the leader defends the wingman; a matter of mutual support.

Although it was Von Richtofen who so successfully exploited his opponent's vulnerability to the rear, caused by the lack of mutual cross-cover, it was in 1915 that Von Richtofen's one-time instructor, Oswalde Boelcke, together with Max Immelman, developed, documented and finally taught the principles of air tactics and the basic formation manoeuvres which have served fighter pilots so well since. Their work was all the more impressive because of the problems they had to overcome, perhaps the greatest of which was the lack of any communication system between the aircraft in a formation, something taken for granted today. In 1915 a series of hand signals and wing waggling had to suffice. The system served them well, because the ranges between the aircraft in a formation tended to be small; the performance of aircraft at that time was such that if distances were too large, mutual support was impossible to provide, even if a threat had been identified. The same relationship between performance and formation distance can be seen today. Conversely, the very tight turn radii of the slow biplanes allowed Max Immelman to develop the famous Immelman turn; a half-loop with a roll-off-the-top, which confronted the uninitiated enemy with an opponent approaching from high head-on despite starting from a position of severe disadvantage (Fig. 3.9).

The requirement for the formation derived, therefore, from the need to cover the blind area to the rear, and particularly to the low rear. The degree of this blind area depends greatly on the individual aircraft design; aircraft with highly faired cockpits, the MiG-21 and the F-4, have generally poor rearward view. The more modern fighters, designed with air superiority dogfighting in mind, the F-16 and F-18, tend to have cockpits standing well proud of the fuselage, allowing excellent rearward vision. Notwithstanding such design, the intervention of the fuselage structure still prevents view to the low rear, which remains a vulnerable direction.

Formation tactics developed only slowly during World War I. This is hardly surprising when the aircraft started out as merely an observation device, with few giving thought to its use as a weapon system in its own right. The air combat scene may be said to have started on 5 October 1914, the day that Corporal Louis

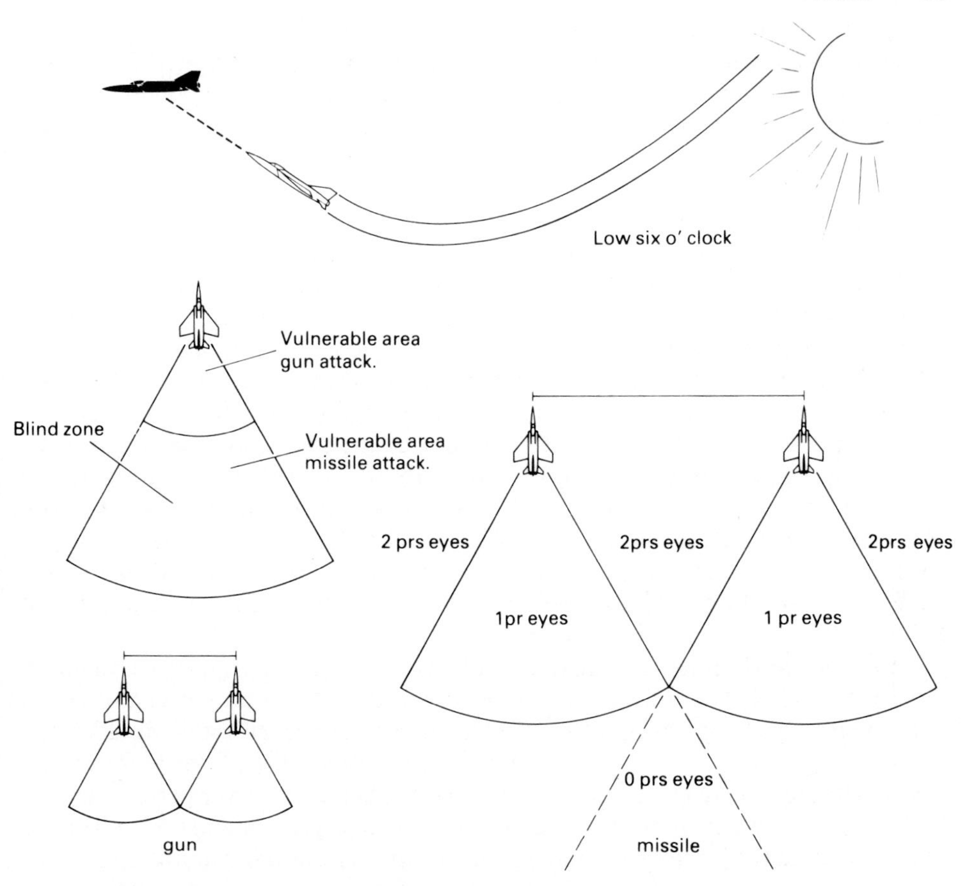

FIG. 3.8. Formation panel.

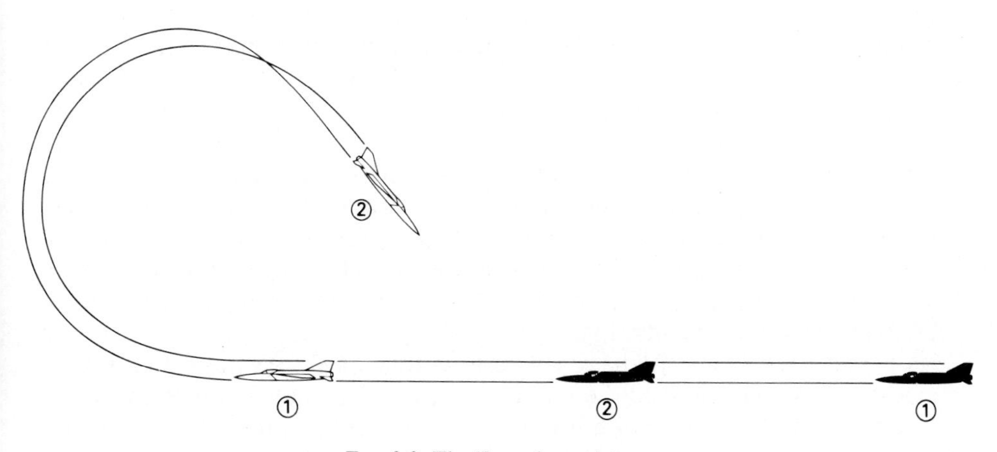

FIG. 3.9. The 'Immelmann' turn.

Quenault, the observer in a French Voisin, piloted by Sergeant Joseph Frantz, engaged a German Aviatrik with a machine gun and shot it down. For a time thereafter air combat was undertaken much in the manner of the man-of-war in full sail; flying alongside the enemy and exchanging fire sideways. This led to the mounting of fixed forward-firing machine guns, usually well above the pilot on the top wing surface, which eased the problem of the pilot but nonetheless made sighting very difficult. This situation applied until a breakthrough occurred, a step increase in effectiveness, which was the invention of the interrupter gear allowing the machine gun to be mounted in the pilot's sight line and to fire through the rotating propeller.

During the inter-war period, remarkably little tactical development took place in the established air forces, and fighters regularly operated during the later years of peace in either a close vic formation or a close finger-form formation. In both of these formations a disproportionate amount of the pilot's attention had to be given to the task of flying in close proximity to the other aircraft, and little could be spared for lookout. Furthermore, all the aircraft in such a formation were so close that they all had effectively the same blind areas; there was negligible cross-over, particularly to the rear. Unbelievably, it was with formations such as these that the RAF started World War II, and were in common use up to the time of the Battle of Britain.

It took the newly emerged Luftwaffe, spurred on by their practical experience in the Spanish Civil War of the late 1930s, to see the merit in a looser formation with greatly enhanced cross-cover. Under the influence of Willi Molders, the 'Schwarm' formation was born and this was the precursor of battle formation today. Although there are many variations on the theme due to the performance of both friendly and enemy aircraft, weapon parameters, weather and such, all utilise the fundamental principles of the Schwarm, that is mutual support and cross-cover.

The heavily laden, and therefore relatively unmanoeuvrable, fighter-bomber aircraft have had to modify their formations to accommodate their particular requirements. If they are intercepted and have to violently manoeuvre or to combat defending fighters, it is unlikely that their fuel states will allow them to continue to their targets. Defensive fighters can capitalise on this to their advantage, and by merely forcing penetrating aircraft to counter their feint attacks can prevent their progress and in so doing can perfectly defend the target. Equally, if weapon shots can be made which force the attackers to exploit their maximum performance manoeuvre, they may find it necessary to jettison their external stores to do so. Again, the target is thereby perfectly defended.

The attacker is looking, therefore, for a formation which assists attack progression, lowers the chance of interception and gives a high chance of obtaining kills of the defending fighters while not engaging in high-energy manoeuvring. The CARD formation, and its various derivatives, has proved highly successful in fulfilling these requirements (Fig. 3.10).

As its name suggests, the basic card formation, Card-4, is flown in a square, much as the arrangements of the pips on a card. Unlike other formations, where the position of the aircraft within the formation can be quite critical, in card a considerable amount of flexibility can be accommodated. The distances apart

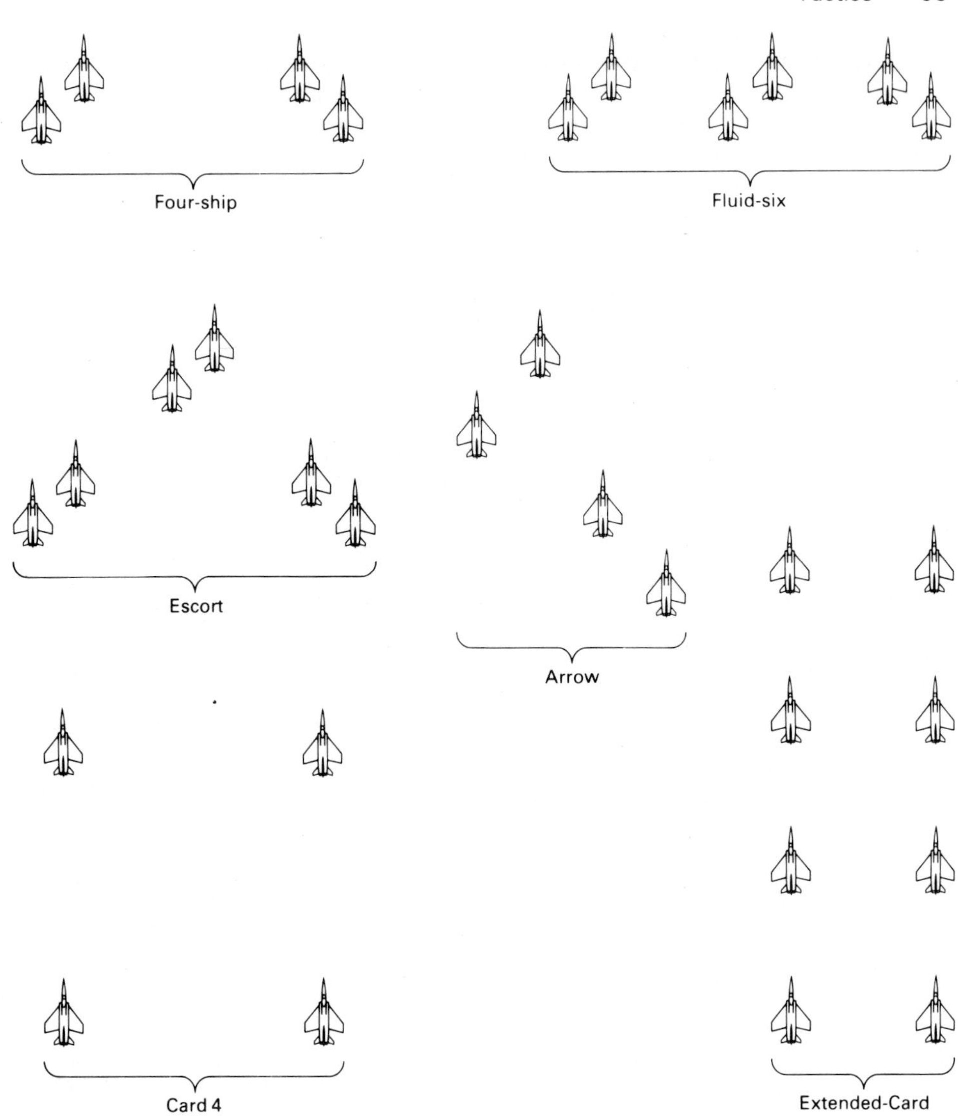

FIG. 3.10. Varieties of formations.

laterally will be governed by visibility, terrain and the ability to mutually support the other formation members, rather than by any convention. Longitudinally, the separation is again fluid, but driven more by the requirement to be able to close to a weapon shot on any intruding fighter attacking the aircraft in front. Consequently, the separations in a card formation can be very large, and not infrequently there will be 4 km between aircraft laterally and something only a little less longitudinally if the attackers are missile-armed. If only gun-armed, the distances are necessarily much reduced.

There are many advantages of card formation over previous battle formations. It allows for greater manoeuvrability, with each aircraft able to use its maximum turn performance without reducing the defensive integrity of the formation (Fig. 3.11). In other battle formations the leader must always allow some performance margin to allow other members to play the geometry of the turn. If he fails to do this, the individual elements will tend to end up in line astern rather than line abreast and be vulnerable to the stern attack. In Card-4 all four aircraft can turn at maximum rate and will end up in Card-4.

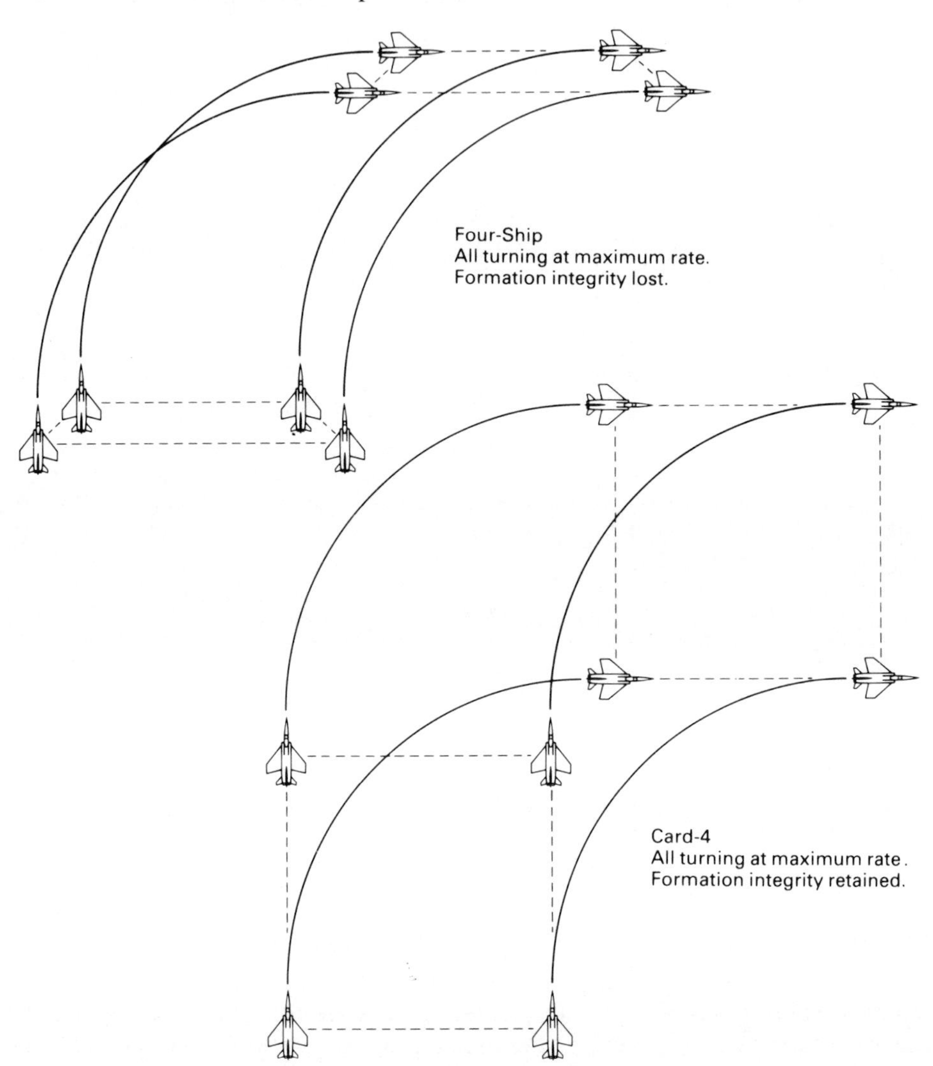

FIG. 3.11. Four-ship and Card-4.

Because of the wide separations involved, and particularly so when used at low altitude by well-camouflaged aircraft, it is very difficult for a fighter making a visual attack to spot all the aircraft in a card formation. If he sights one aircraft and assumes it is a singleton, and commits to an attack, he is more than likely to offer an easy shot to an unseen attacker. If he suspects that he might be attacking a card formation, he may have to wait until he is quite sure that he is aware of the position of all the formation members before attacking. This can take time, which is all to the advantage of the penetrators, and can require paralleling the penetration track to work down the formation to find the end aircraft. While paralleling the track, the fighter is vulnerable to attack from penetrators diverging from the stream to take advantage of the opportunity shot. The fighter pilot must never become complacent in attacking a penetrating formation. The term *fighter*-bomber is well chosen, and when the occasion presents itself the fighter-bomber pilot will show all the verve, élan, initiative and aggression traditionally associated with the fighter pilot.

A source of confusion for the fighter is that card formation is not restricted to four aircraft, it can be extended to very large numbers. In this case it is difficult for the fighter to engage without presenting a chance for a shot to the penetrators. If he is prudent, and waits until he is sure he knows the position of all the aircraft involved in an extended card formation, he may take many minutes, and then not be sure, and at a progression at penetrating speed of 7 or 8 nm/min not too many minutes can be squandered before attacking lest the target is reached and the defence rendered ineffective.

Card formation does much to counter the performance advantage of the fighter. It does so by optimising the mutual support emanating from large numbers. As it is used to best effect in mass, it matches perfectly the requirement for saturation attack. A further advantage is that at such wide separations large areas about the other formation members are visually covered. This not only makes it difficult for a fighter to engage without being seen, but also allows the individual crews within the card formation to spend more of their time on flying their own aircraft rather than having to concentrate on the more difficult task of holding the closer formation positions. This allows aircraft within a card formation to be flown generally lower than would be the case in most other formations, and the increased distances remove much of the danger of slip stream from other formation aircraft. Slip stream at low level can be vicious, leading to overstressed aircraft and even to temporary loss of control as the wake is traversed.

By flying lower, the possibility of skylining waiting Combat Air Patrol (CAP) aircraft is increased. This is a considerable advantage and a low-flying attacker can spot a high-flying CAP aircraft at long range, not exceptionally as much as a minutes flying time away. This opens up options. The formation can stay on track and hope that they are not visually acquired. With small formations, this can happen quite often. Or a diversion from track can be made to place more distance between formation and CAP to make acquisition more difficult, or the diversion could be made to take advantage of terrain screening, or to fly over terrain which would better match the camouflage scheme being used.

Before attack aircraft were fitted with air-to-air missiles, the defence-avoidance options were to be favoured; the primary duty of an attack aircraft is to successfully engage the target, not to be waylaid by air combat. However, a missile-armed attacker can find in such circumstances that he is provided with an easy chance shot and, depending on the strength of the fighter CAP, may be unwise not to take the kill. There will always be debate on this issue by attack leaders, and the case for and against engaging can be argued convincingly by both sides. As with most things, it is highly scenario-dependent. Where there should be less debate is what should be done if the same opportunity is presented after the primary target has been engaged. The CAP aircraft then becomes a bonus or additional target, and the attack aircraft, with less fuel and weapons, is better placed to take an opportunity shot and to continue to egress.

This highlights a new situation brought about by the fitment of air-to-air missiles on attack aircraft that needs to be noted by both attack and fighter aircraft. Once the weight and drag of weapons are removed post-target, the modern attack aircraft is a perfectly capable fighter and should be planned to be used as such. This is particularly so as it will be returning to base light, armed and otherwise unencumbered, in the same direction as the enemy attack aircraft will be heading outbound, but they will be heavy, slow and ponderous. If friendly attack aircraft on egress can get amongst hostile attack aircraft during their ingress phase, there should be easy pickings to be had.

The missile-armed attack aircraft presents a further problem to the defensive fighter other than that posed by formation mutual support. Once the weapons and external tanks have been jettisoned to counter a determined attack, the attack aircraft can be effectively transformed into a far more competent fighter in its own right. Fighter pilots tend to fall into the trap of assuming that tactics which work in peace, where attack aircraft are prevented from jettisoning their loads, will equally work in war. It could be a dangerous assumption in the age of the missile-armed attack aircraft, and fighters should always plan their attack with options in mind for countering an aircraft which suddenly achieves a much enhanced performance envelope by jettisoning.

It is difficult for a defending fighter to know which target the fighter-bomber is attacking, and therefore how close he is to releasing his weapons. If the formation is penetrating at reasonably high speeds at low level, it is very difficult for even the most high-performance fighter to make slashing attacks from the side. The speed margin is insufficient to do so, because even the fastest fighters tend to be limited at low level to indicated airspeeds around 700 kts. A large overtake speed is required to successfully conduct quarter attacks, let alone considerable skill to execute them at low altitudes. The result is that if the penetrating formation can maintain a high penetration speed, or increase speed when threatened by fighters, the fighters will tend to be drawn increasingly into the direct 6 o'clock position. The fighters, in turn, will hope that their missiles will acquire without the need for them to close to the 6 o'clock position, but at very low levels missile lock can be problematical.

Once in the 6 o'clock, weapons released by the fighter-bombers on the target can result in a large debris hemisphere being thrown up in the face of the pursuing fighter; unnerving at worse and fatal at best.

Low altitude is in itself a defence for the attack aircraft against fighters and the attack crew must use it whenever possible to remove from the fighter the ability to use the third dimension. A cloud overcast helps to prevent the fighter using the third dimension for positioning or for escape from a foiled attack. At high level the vertical is used extensively in air combat, be that in close combat or in interception. Soviet writings also mention that in the past 80 per cent of aircraft successfully engaged were attacked by aircraft which they did not see, and in this they agree with Western assessments. However, they go further and say that of these, 75 per cent were attacked by aircraft remaining unseen by use of the vertical.

It is quite usual for aircraft at high level, using the vertical, to fly up and down through the target altitude, and many tactical options rely upon it; at other times it is unavoidable. The attack aircraft operating at low level, however, takes away from the fighter half of his vertical and cloud overcasts can take away the other half, confining the interaction to two dimensions. This is of great advantage to the attack aircraft. If the fighter wishes to remain engaged and in contact with an attack formation proceeding under a low overcast, he may have to limit his speed and restrict his attacks to those where the escape manoeuvre will keep him clear of cloud. Once having entered a low cloud base it can be hazardous attempting to regain contact with the ground, more so in the likely presence of missile-armed attack aircraft. To regain ground contact away from the fighters, or to seek assistance to do so, all takes time, and time assists the attackers to penetrate further towards the target.

The threat most to be feared by the attack formation is the look-down-shoot-down (LDSD) missile from beyond visual range. A very manoeuvrable formation is required to successfully counter such an attack. The fighter needs to identify the target on radar and may need to position carefully for a successful attack. As the radar will be looking down into ground clutter, pulse doppler techniques are most likely to be used. This technique relies on identifying by radar signal-processing targets with a velocity difference, using the same principle which gives the change in tone to a train whistle as it passes at speed past an observer. The ground returns, which have no speed, are ignored and targets having a closure speed of their own are displayed. To avoid showing targets which have speed but which are not practical targets, and this may include helicopters or fast-moving vehicles on autobahns, pulse doppler radars usually have a closure speed below which the return is not displayed. Further, the closure speed used in the processing is that aligned to the fighter flight path, that is approaching or receding from the fighter. When interrogating an approaching attack aircraft head-on, this closure speed can be very high, amounting to the sum of both fighter and target speeds. But if the fighter radar transmissions can be detected on the radar-warning receiver of the attack aircraft, and a turn is executed to place the fighter indication on the beam, then the target speed is now perpendicular to the fighter flight path and the closure speed falls below the cut-off (Fig. 3.12). The fighter would then lose lock and have to position for a further attack. This takes time, during which the attack formation can resume track and proceed further to the target. This technique works well against systems where missiles home onto the reflected radiation from the fighter radar. The technique would be less straightforward against active missiles such as AMRAAM.

A difficult part of the mission in which to maintain mutual support and cover is the approach to the target from the initial point to the time when the formation has been reconstituted after the attack. The ability of the formation to maintain integrity is governed by the demands of weaponeering and the avoidance of self-damage, and this is covered later.

Advocates of the more traditional form of formation, the leader and wingman operating under close and well-defined parameters, took some time before they

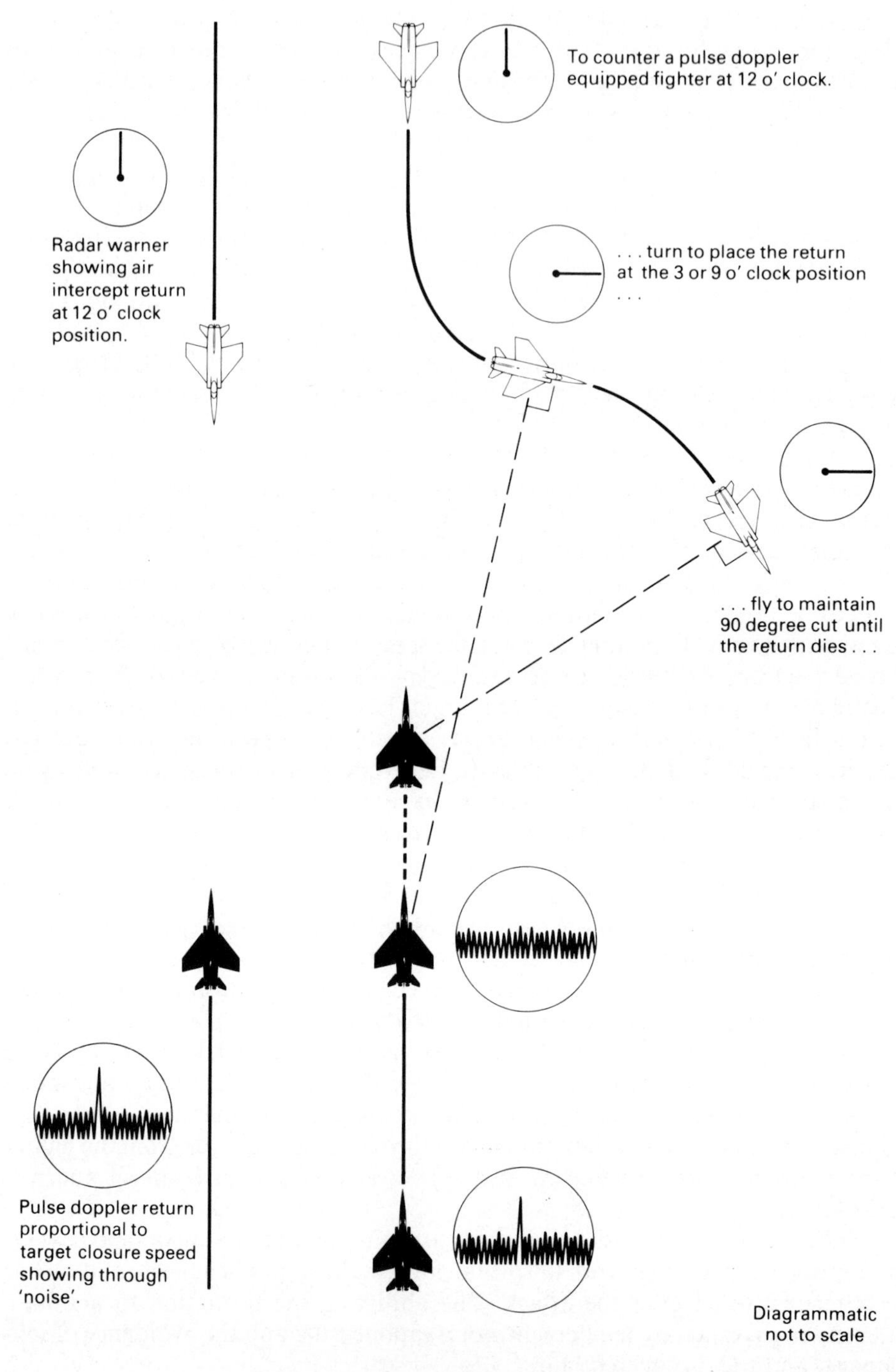

FIG. 3.12. Pulse doppler and the counter.

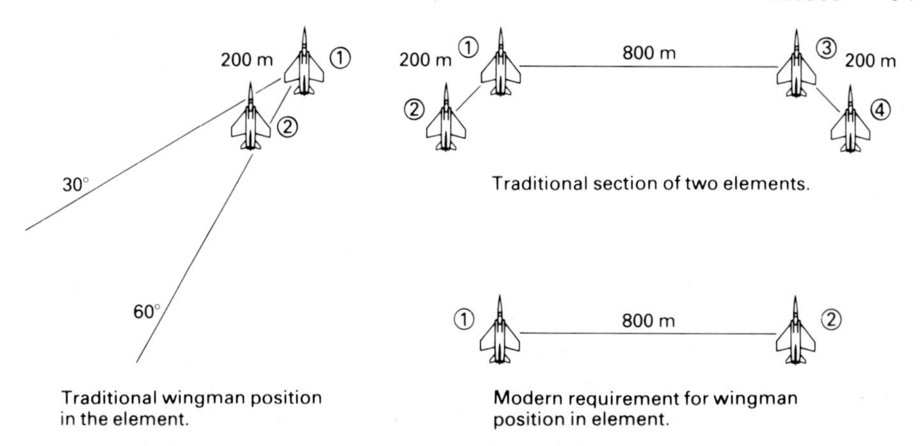

FIG. 3.13. Wingman positions.

accepted the new loose, less stylised forms of formation. They had their point; as in most debate, the truth is rarely to be found in the black or white of the extreme, but in the less specific greys between. The case was made that the traditional formation position for a wingman, swept some 30–60° and holding a position about 200 m from the leader, was an excellent place from which the junior man might study his leader, learn from his example and develop his own art (Fig. 3.13).

There is much to be said for this, particularly so in circumstances such as those existing in World War II where pilot losses, and the subsequent high replacement rates, meant that pilots were joining squadrons with only one-third of the hours which would be the norm today. New pilots joining squadrons during the Battle of Britain, for example, sometimes had little more than 80 hr, and only a handful of hours on type, before being thrown into combat. In such circumstances, being 'led by the hand' by a more experienced man was an advantage and must have been something of a comfort to the new arrival. On the other hand, a pilot of such limited experience must have spent the majority of his time and ability merely holding position on a more experienced leader in the confusion of a combat, and how well, or otherwise, he performed his primary task of lookout, particularly for threats against the rear, is questionable. One or two 'aces' ended their war with reputations for regularly losing their wingmen, but was this surprising? If the 'ace' was such because he could outmanoeuvre his opponent, then he was placing a very high demand on his wingmen to *stick, search* and *report*, the three cardinal rules laid down for junior fighter pilots. In retrospect, it is encouraging that so many did so well, it was certainly verging on the unreasonable to ask for such performance following the abbreviated training.

The inherent difficulty in sticking, searching and reporting, leading as it did to poor rearward lookout, was only one of the disadvantages of the classic wingman position. Another was the lack of firepower caused by the wingman hardly ever being able to bring his guns to bear in a manoeuvring combat and only to do so against an unmanoeuvring target at the cost of degraded rearward cover while concentration was tunnelled upon the gunsight. Perhaps the reason this formation existed for so long, and was advocated so loud, was that it fitted best in the interceptor role, the combat against bomber formations which were unmanoeuvrable and non-aggressive. This was largely seen to be the role of the RAF between the wars and would account in some way for the lack of tactical air combat development in the inter-war period. After all, why practice combat and develop fighter vs fighter tactics when the Messerschmidts over the Rhine were out of range? It was when those same ME-109s were based at Calais, and when the bomber formations were escorted by fighters, that the wasteful years were made apparent and tactical doctrine had to be rewritten in the heat of battle.

It was the advent of missile-armed fighters which started the move towards fundamental revision of the traditional wingman formation. The missile threat forced the wingman to fly further and further out from his leader to cover the greatly increased threat range to the rear. As he moved further out, so he had to reduce the sweepback on the leader if he was to get any rear cover himself. Instead of flying as the wingman in an 'element', the basic formation unit of two aircraft, the wingman had to fly much as though he was an element leader himself.

Offensively the missile equally imposed its own demand for change. In one sense the missile offered the chance to overcome the constraint on fire power from the wingman. But this could only be exploited if the wingman could be quite sure that when he released his missile it was locked onto the enemy rather than his leader. In the early days of infrared (IR) missiles it was difficult to be certain which target was locked on if there was more than one in the missile's angle of view. To fire safely, therefore, the wingman needed to be well clear of his leader's tail and in a position not only to lay his own attack but to be able to assess the geometry of the combat overall.

The introduction of radar missiles, many capable of beyond-visual-range performance, caused even the doubters to concede that flying two aircraft in close proximity was to waste fire power and to jeopardise overall situation awareness. Particularly, in the formations of the day, even with the wingman flying well spread, the radar and, of greater impact, the highly capable radar missile could not cover the rear. Yet the enemy were also increasing their missile range, and it was becoming progressively more difficult to cover the vulnerable rear cone by visual means alone. This situation has led to development in tactical doctrine and in equipment; the requirements for missile-approach-warning equipment emerge from this situation, and the Airborne Warning and Control System (AWACS) assists greatly in giving long-range threat warning.

The formation to emerge from the new situation was a product of the Vietnam era and was termed *'Loose Duce'*. The idea is that once combat is initiated, rather than stay as a pair and so inhibit the wingman, both aircraft would operate with a considerable amount of independence but within a co-ordinated tactical plan. It involved one aircraft engaging the enemy in manoeuvre while the other gained energy and engaged subsequently with an advantage. Ideally, one aircraft would always be looking into the fight, so providing more comprehensive cover and more able to lay and lock his longer-ranged weapons. It was a tactical option which closely paralleled the point made before, often in jest but with its serious side, that the best way for a back-seater in a two-place aircraft to cover the rear is to sit such that he looks that way. In two aircraft, if they are heading for each other nose-to-nose, their ability to cover the tail of the other is greatly enhanced (Fig. 3.14).

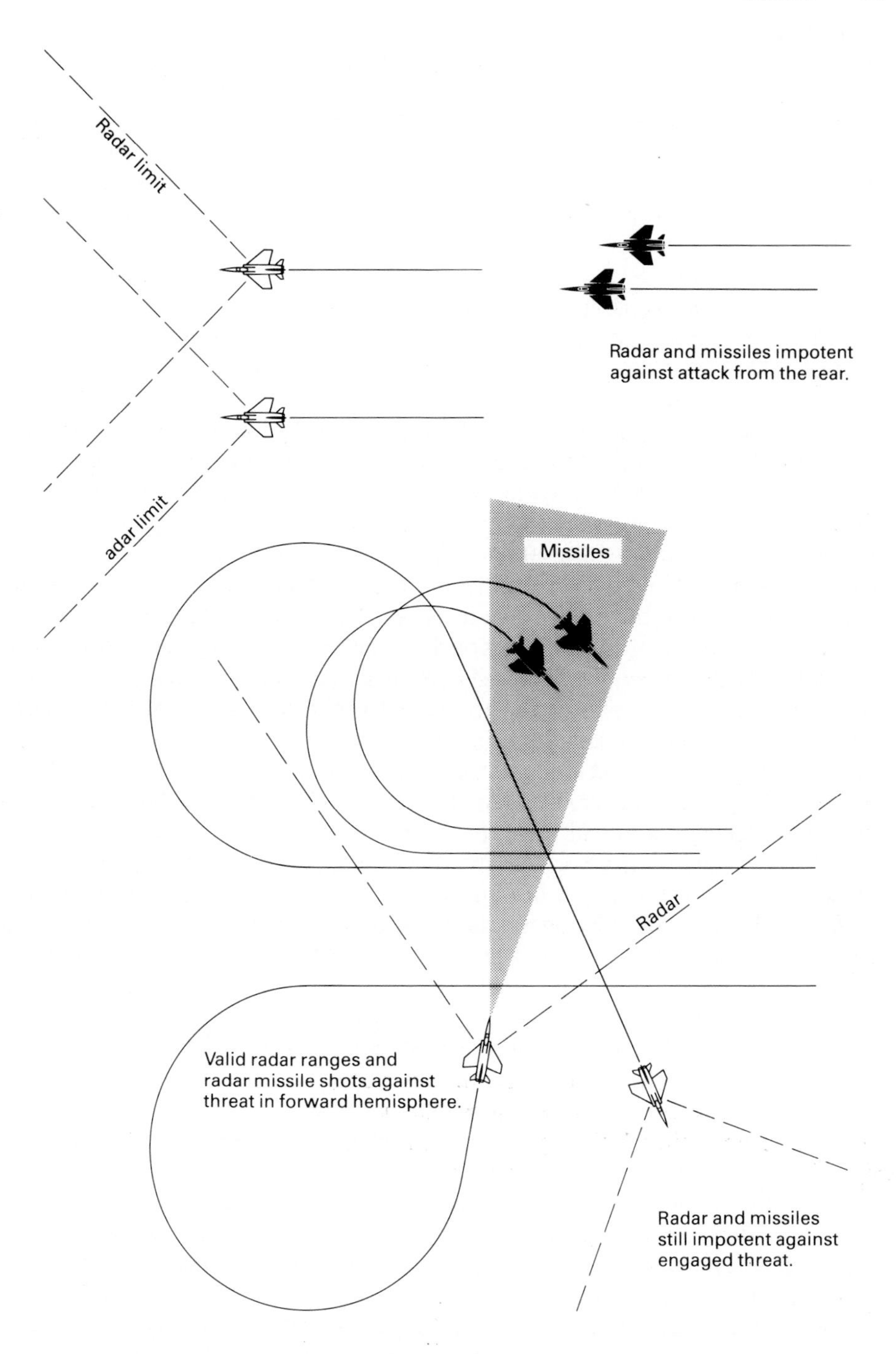

FIG. 3.14. The 'Loose Duce'.

The requirement for widespread elements and for tactical innovation along the lines of the 'Loose Duce' came less from tacticians seeking any perfect combat truth as from the pressure placed upon tactical doctrine by the march of technology. The widespread element was the doctrinal answer to missile ranges extending the vulnerable cone to the rear; the 'Loose Duce' was the doctrinal answer to the need to maintain the ability to use radar and forward-hemisphere missiles and to find some way of maintaining high-energy states while engaged in combat. It was technology which dictated the pace of tactical and doctrinal change, not the other way round, and it is difficult to see how this relationship can change to any marked degree in the future.

Nothing is simple, and there are complications to the most straightforward military scheme; the new and more flexible formations are no exception. Although new crews arrive on squadrons much better trained than their Battle of Britain counterparts, they fly far more complex and demanding aircraft in a more lethal battlefield. Not only must the modern combat pilot be a good pure flier, but he must have a good working knowledge of a wide range of technologies: electronic warfare, radar, missiles, warhead effects, to name but some. Upon joining the squadron, there is still a finite time needed for the new man to learn his art, and thereby lies the difficulty. Many of the new tactics demand much more of the new junior pilot than did the old. In a widespread element the wingman must fly with all the skill and perception previously expected only of more senior and experienced element leaders. In card formation he may fly beyond the range at which effective supervision can be given from more experienced formation members. In 'Loose Duce' the wingman can not only be going in different directions to his leader but when he can see the geometry of the flight, which may be building up in his leaders blind area to the rear, he is expected to take *de facto* control of the flight and call the appropriate tactics.

To bring a new pilot up to the standard necessary to exploit the advantages offered by the new doctrine will require time. Two factors conspire against this: the first is the amount of flying available to squadron pilots in these days of high operating costs. Thirty years ago a young pilot was disappointed to get less than 30 hr a month, now he will be fortunate to get 20 hr a month, and many air forces throughout the world fly their fast-jet crews considerably less than this. It takes time, therefore, to build up corporate skill on a squadron.

In itself this is no major problem; it merely makes the achievement of operational proficiency by a new squadron a more elongated affair than before, but if, once operational, the squadron was left undisturbed, then its proficiency could be consolidated and standards steadily improved. In the West, however, there is a personnel management factor which works heavily against this ideal; the career structure in some air forces demand planned career patterns including for the more junior ranks experience in facets of air force management above and beyond flying. This can cause severe personnel turbulence and in many cases prevents the consolidation necessary for squadrons to bring on their junior crews to full proficiency. There are solutions to this problem, and elements of these can be found in a number of air forces: non-commissioned aircrew, 'limited-career' officers who can spend more time flying and less on staff work, or a career structure which allows officers more time on the front line before accelerating them through the upper ranks. This latter system, having some similarity to the French pattern, has attractions for air forces where technology can leave senior officers outdated if they are too long away from the front line. Whatever system modifications are preferred, a method needs to be found to produce crews with the depth of tactical and system knowledge and, most important, type familiarity to be able to outperform a numerically superior opponent.

In the future the demands upon the crew will become greater and the level of system and tactical knowledge necessary to succeed will be much higher than it is today. 'Formation' as such may be a manoeuvre limited to the entry into and exit out of combat. Once the enemy has been detected, the modern aircraft, a weapons system in its own right, will have to be fought as an individual entity if it is to be exploited to the full. Rather than the waves and wing waggles necessary in the time of Boelcke and Immelman, a new form of communication may be needed, a form far in advance of voice radio which has great inadequacy in conveying large quantities of data. In future the situation plot in the computer of one aircraft will need to be compared and matched with another; one electronic warfare suite will need to communicate with another and perhaps mutually agree on which should jam and which should stay silent, decisions which will need to be taken in timescales far beyond the capacity of any human brain; data from a number of aircraft may have to be fused and a collated picture disseminated to them all before the best attack plan can be derived, and that may in part, or in whole, be determined by computer software. It may be a long time before the close-in, multi-aircraft combat can be fully automated; it is a much shorter timescale before the longer-ranged BVR or air-intercept mission can be mechanised.

4

Tactical Nuclear Operations

Nuclear weapons, and even nuclear energy, following the incidents at Three Mile Island and at Chernobyl, raise the passions equally of those in favour as for those against. The awesome power available for use in good or evil is frightening to many and their sensibilities must be respected. Much of the fear of the nuclear weapon or nuclear energy comes from ignorance of what it is, how it works and from the, at times, sterile debate about its abolition which too often clouds the real issues. Whether a rational thinking mankind would invent or discover the nuclear reactor with the benefit of hindsight is a subject for a more esoteric work than this. From a military man's viewpoint, it remains as a fact; the nuclear weapon has been invented, it cannot be disinvented, and whatever the rights or wrongs it becomes part of the weapon inventory. It therefore has to be considered, studied, planned for and accepted.

The comments here are, however, restricted to those relating to the use of the nuclear weapon on the battlefield. The views are strictly those of the author and no hidden endorsement of positions various should be read into them. Further, the nuclear weapon, because of its enormity, is something the military man may apply, but always under the strictest political control. The nuclear weapon is primarily a political weapon and the decision to use it or otherwise will always be jealously guarded by the political authorities; and right and proper that is in a democracy. In this chapter therefore, no political commentary is made and the reader will search to no avail for it.

In 1945 two aircraft, of the tens of thousands employed throughout World War II, one over Hiroshima and the over Nagasaki, brought to an end a conflict which had cost the world an estimated 40 million casualties. While armies massed and fleets stood poised, it was air power which administered the *coup de grâce.*

Each of the weapons dropped on Japan had a yield of about 13 kilotons (kT) or the equivalent explosive power of 13,000 tons of high explosive. Their effect was dramatic. It was meant to be. It had to convince the Japanese that resistance was pointless and that capitulation in the face of such a terrible weapon was excusable. Some argue that it was for this reason that Hiroshima and Nagasaki were selected as targets. Hiroshima was a city built predominantly of lightly constructed dwellings with a high timber content. There were few buildings in the modern idiom of steel and concrete. It was a city largely unwarned of the air attack and, of course, quite unprepared for a nuclear attack. The result was an estimated 70,000 casualties. To keep the attack in perspective, however, it must be looked upon alongside the attacks on targets such as Tokyo, Hamburg and Dresden, where effects quite as impressive resulted from conventional, more understandable, and consequently less frightening or pressworthy, attack.

When discussing the use of nuclear weapons, more so on the battlefield, it is important to keep in mind their physical properties, their effects on likely targets and the relationship between size, or yield, and accuracy.

Before considering in more detail the effects of nuclear weapons on the battlefield and some of the means of delivering them, it is first necessary to consider the effect they have on tactical doctrine and on the options open to a commander engaged in an adventure in north-west Europe against the NATO alliance.

In facing a Warsaw Pact, directed by the traditional military doctrine of the Soviet Union, calling as it does for the full exploitation of *mass* and *momentum*, the nuclear weapon has been, and to a large extent continues to be, the great leveller. The nuclear weapon counters *mass*, indeed it thrives upon the massed target, and that in turn becomes a considerable constraint on any aggressor wishing to use mass and momentum of his offensive purpose. It has been accepted by conventional wisdom throughout the years that against prepared defences the attacker must concentrate to achieve his ends. The degree of concentration needed will depend on a variety of factors: the quality of the defender in terms of both men and material, the degree of prepared defences, plans and training, the element of surprise, the terrain, the weather, and in this modern age of informed and educated soldiery, perhaps even the rightness of the cause. Some say that it would be imprudent to attack without a superiority locally of three to one; others, that much higher concentrations would be needed to break well-planned defences manned by high-quality troops; at high as ten or even fifteen to one at the cutting edge when faced by determined defenders.

This gives rise to a basic contradiction facing the Soviet planner. He has mass and the military tradition of using it, and as little time ago (in the Soviet psyche) as the Great Patriotic War of 1941–45 it served to great effect from the turn of the tide at Kursk to the gates of the Reichstag and beyond. He also knows that he must concentrate to achieve his breakthrough. He is also aware that his doctrine calls for units optimised for offensive action, but with less staying power than Western equivalents; the Soviet unit fights to exhaustion and is then replaced from the rear by fresh troops. Only in this manner can the great momentum be maintained, but the cost is in the necessity for secure and high-capacity lines of communication.

If units cannot mass in peace because of the threat of nuclear strike, then they must be dispersed, but in a manner which allows for the necessary offensive concentration. This is one of the reasons for the Warsaw Pact system of echeloning which sees divisions running from close to the inner German border through the satellite states into the western military districts of the Soviet Union. The posture is a fair defence against the pre-emptive nuclear attack, but imposes a reliance on reliable lines of communication which themselves become vulnerable to interdiction.

To lessen the reliance on vulnerable lines of communication, a military planner would wish to stockpile heavy or bulky stores as far forward as possible, and there is evidence that the Warsaw Pact have adopted this sensible course, but stocks held forward, unless widely dispersed or heavily protected, become vulnerable targets in their own right. It is a predicament which illustrates staff college teaching that most military options have both advantages and disadvantages; the skill is to exploit the one while minimising the other.

Looked at this way, and from the Soviet viewpoint, certain developments become more understandable. There has been much debate on the appearance in recent years of both the Soviet Operational Manoeuvre Groups (OMG) and the resources being expended on battlefield helicopters. At times the debate has been convoluted to a fault and at others suggesting the influence of some Machiavellian mind formulating a master chess move which is beyond Western comprehension. Looked upon from a Soviet perception, both developments are quite straightforward and derive almost automatically from the circumstances.

If a commander is forced to disperse, or echelon, to prevent the pre-emptive nuclear strike, yet has to concentrate to advance in the face of prepared and well-equipped defences, the time spent moving from one state to the other must be kept to an absolute minimum. The move forward of troops by air to mate with their equipment already stockpiled forward is one method of achieving the aim; the use of railways in the true Bismarck tradition, allowing troops and heavy equipment to move forward faster than under their own arrangements, is another; ensuring that units are fully mechanised is yet another, accepting that in an intense, highly dynamic conflict the cutting arm of the Red Army, the armour, cannot afford to pause for its infantry and artillery support to catch up. The whole must be able to move as an integrated whole.

Mobility and speed fall out as natural requirements from the policy of echeloning in the face of the nuclear threat. Speed particularly, not only because this is the element which enables surprise to be obtained, and surprise is a Soviet principle of war quoted most times in first order of precedence, but also because the Soviet sees himself facing an alliance of sixteen sovereign democratic nations to whom the use of nuclear weapons is abhorrent and who can reasonably be expected to take longer over their nuclear release deliberations than would the Soviet-dominated Warsaw Pact. The more mobile targets are, the more difficult they will be for NATO to engage successfully with a nuclear strike.

Once in the forward area, and the final vulnerable concentration is undertaken, the greatest protection from nuclear strike is to engage the enemy as closely as possible so that it is difficult to engage with a nuclear weapon without suffering self-inflicted casualties. The OMG is a useful tool to gain infiltration into defending troops, because it can thrust at speed and the further it can progress into the defender's territory so the more he is forced to use weapons of mass destruction on his own ground and accept the heavy collateral damage to both property and people which this could bring. From a Soviet point of view this would be against the inclination of the capitalistic and moralistic West.

It is from the same premise, that is the need for dispersal, speed in deployment, and concentration for the offensive, that a logical explanation is found for the Soviet development of the attack helicopter. Much time and resource has been put into this field by the Soviets, and their Hind series of battlefield helicopters is probably the best in the world. Those who point to Western technological superiority should look closely at the Hind from a military perspective. A confusion arises in the West, however, in looking upon battlefield helicopters as *aircraft*, whereas clearly their use is as *tanks* and their place in Valhalla will be amongst the cavalry squadrons rather than the air squadrons. They have the punch of a tank, are able to disperse better than tanks over a wider area, they can concentrate quicker than land-based armour and in most respects fit happily into an offensive force which needs to concentrate in the face of nuclear weapons.

But should there be the sometimes irrational fear of nuclear weapons which exists in so many minds? Are they really so terrible that they should bring to war constraints which have never before been considered necessary, or are they overvalued and are better seen as merely bigger and better bombs? After all, pictures of the aftermath in the streets of Hiroshima were quite similar to those taken in Hamburg and Dresden and the lightly built structures proved to be the perfect nuclear demonstration target; yet the modern buildings remained upright and the electric tram service was restored within 48 hrs. 45,000 people were killed during ten nights of 'conventional' bombing of Hamburg and 'tens of thousands' were killed in a single night's fire bombing of Tokyo, some suggest as many as 84,000. Conventional bombing had already assumed impressive proportions, 'thousand bomber' raids had attacked the Third Reich and, despite the geography, 828 Superfortresses attacked Japan during the day and night on 14 August 1945. So what is the nature of the nuclear weapon and how does it relate to the modern battlefield?

The nuclear reaction is produced by either fission, the process of splitting a heavy nucleus, or by fusion, which is the opposite effect of joining lighter nuclei to form a heavier one. In both processes a very large release of energy occurs, and this in turn translates into the destructive effect of the weapon. Fission, associated with the earlier 'atom bombs', is a less effective means of obtaining the energy required and is now not as common as fusion weapons.

Fission weapons are designed to bring a quantity of fissile material to a supercritical state, and this can be achieved by impacting two subcritical masses in a 'tube' or 'gun' arrangement—as was the case in the early Hiroshima bomb (Fig. 4.1)—or by forming the material into a sphere and compressing it to a supercritical state by using surrounding high explosive to 'implode' on the sphere (Fig. 4.2). This latter method allows more economical use of fissile material, but does call for a much higher degree of engineering to obtain the correct and balanced implosion effect.

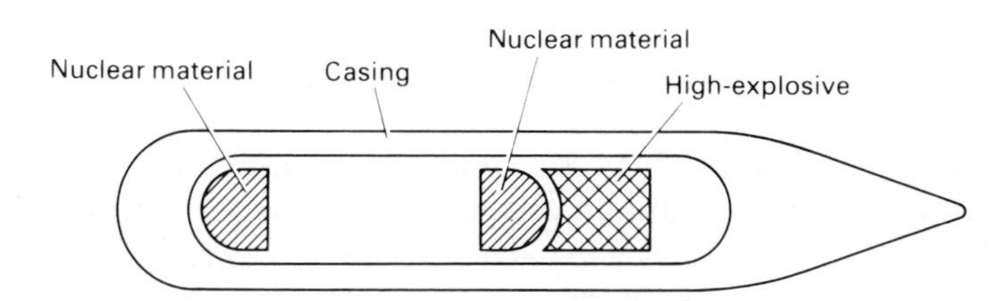

FIG. 4.1. Gun-type nuclear weapon. Similar to that dropped on Hiroshima and giving rise to the name the 'thin-man' or 'Little Boy' bomb.

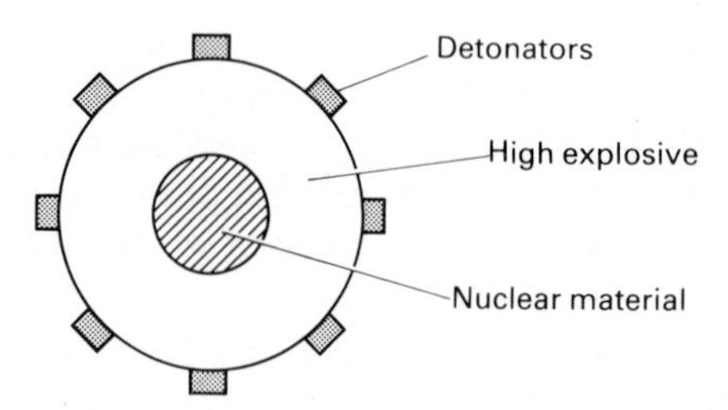

FIG. 4.2. A fusion weapon uses implosion techniques which require advanced engineering to ensure that the shock waves act together at the centre where the nuclear material is positioned. Failure to do so will result in the weapon being blown apart from the high-explosive effect and the nuclear material spread as contamination. A nuclear explosion will not result.

A fusion weapon requires extremely high temperatures to initiate and sustain the reaction, and a fission reaction is used as an initiator. The yield from a fusion weapon is in the order of three times as great as from a fission weapon, but because the problem of obtaining critical mass is absent, there is less limit to the size of the weapon and, thereby, the yield produced. Fusion weapons can be therefore of very high yield and the 58-megaton (MT) weapon exploded by the Soviet Union is thought to be the largest device tested to date. In fusion weapons some 85–90 per cent of the energy released is in the form of heat, which gives rise to the thermal and blast effects of the weapon, and something over 5 per cent in radiation.

It is possible to design warheads where the energy released as heat is reduced and that by radiation considerably enhanced. These are the so-called *enhanced radiation* or *neutron* weapons which captured the headlines in the late 1970s and early 1980s.

It is useful to have in mind an idea of the size of nuclear warheads before discussing their effects. When Colonel Paul Tibbetts took off from Tinian on 6 August 1945 at 0245 hr his aircraft carried the large and unwieldy 'Little Boy' bomb of 13 kT capacity, the equivalent of 13,000 tons of TNT. Now weapons are far smaller and can be fired from artillery pieces. From first principles it can be estimated that if 1 g of high explosive is equal to about 1000 cal of energy, then about 0.047 g of U^{235}, completely fissioned, equates to the energy of 1 ton of high explosive. From this about 47 kg of U^{235} would produce a 1 MT explosion, or the equivalent of 1,000,000 tons of high explosive. But as a large surrounding mass of fissile material is required to initiate and sustain the reaction, the weight of the weapon will be larger than this. If this surrounding structure is assumed to be, say, ten times the weight of the primary material, then a total weight of the warhead of about 500 kg is suggested. Even with an allowance added for fuzing, aerodynamic structure and firing circuits, the overall weight of a 1-MT weapon should still remain well within the bracket normally associated with conventional bombs in the 1000–2000-lb class.

Another approach assumes that 1 lb of uranium or plutonium will yield about 8 kT in fission, while 1 lb of deuterium will yield about 26 kT in fusion. It is unlikely that this theoretical 100 per cent efficiency would be achieved in practice, but nonetheless it serves to reinforce the message that nuclear weapons need not be physically large.

The effects of a nuclear explosion are five-fold: there is the fireball, the radioactive debris forming the characteristic cloud, the shockwave and blast effect, the radiation of heat and intense light, and the invisible rays and particles. The rays and particles are known more commonly as nuclear radiation, and the heat and light effects are known as thermal radiation. The radiation is further divided between that which is emitted at, or very soon after, the moment of the explosion, and that which is emitted for long periods afterwards from the radioactive products produced by the explosion.

THE FIREBALL

At the moment of detonation the weapon produces a reaction which causes the temperature to rise to tens of millions of degrees, this in turn resulting in tremendous pressures. Within less than a millionth of a second the high-temperature, high-pressure core of the explosion radiates energy, mainly in the form of X-rays, which when absorbed by the surrounding atmosphere forms a hot luminous spherical mass known as the fireball.

Because the size of the fireball depends upon the absorbtion of the X-rays in air, and that depends on the density of the air, fireballs produced from any given size of weapon tend to increase in size with altitude. For example, a 1-MT warhead will produce a 1-km diameter fireball at sea level, but if this warhead was detonated at 15,000 m altitude, the fireball would be 2.1 km in diameter; at 60,000 m it would be 21.3 km in diameter. The diameter of the fireball created by a nuclear explosion can be estimated using the following formulae:

$$D=\left(Y\frac{P_1}{P_0}\right)^{\frac{1}{3}}$$

where Y=warhead yield in megatons,
D=fireball diameter,
$\frac{P_1}{P_0}$=ratio of atmospheric densities at sea level and at the explosion altitude. This in turn is given by:

$$\frac{P_1}{P_0}=e^{h}/6,600$$

where h=explosion altitude in metres.

Above altitudes of about 60,000 m, the atmosphere becomes progressively thinner and the above formula becomes increasingly less accurate in forecasting fireball diameters. Explosions still have their purpose at such heights. The mass of electrons produced by the explosion now exist without the same atmospheric attenuation and can be dense enough to seriously affect radar and radio transmissions. This is the so-called 'black-out' effect (Fig. 4.3) which could be used itself as a means of affecting the early-warning sensors guarding against ballistic missile attack. Very substantial black areas can be produced by large weapons detonated at very high altitudes.

Near the ground, the factor P_1/P_0 becomes unity and the diameter of the fireball becomes more nearly $Y^{\frac{1}{3}}$. The radius of destruction on the ground, as represented

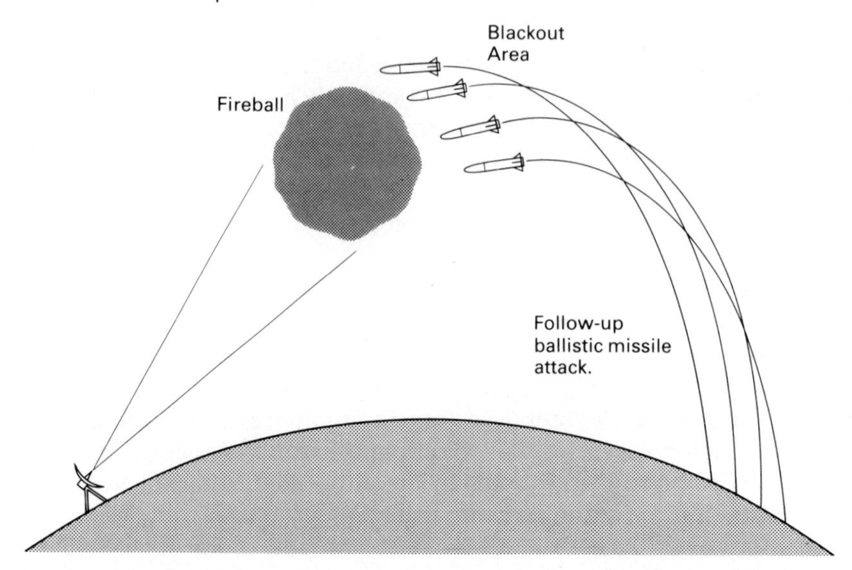

FIG. 4.3. The explosion of a nuclear weapon at very high altitudes produces a dense electron environment which prevents the transmission of radar and radio wavelengths. The phenomenon could be used to shield the approach of ballistic missiles.

by the edge of the fireball, will be $\frac{1}{2}\ Y^{\frac{1}{3}}$ and can be related to the height of the burst by:

$$r^2+h^2=\tfrac{1}{4}\ Y^{\frac{2}{3}}.$$

A 1-MT explosion will produce a radius of destruction of about 0.5 km at sea level, but will barely touch the surface if detonated 0.5 km high. For small nuclear weapons overpressure is the main destructive mechanism, and this decreases as the cube of the distance from the point of explosion. This indicates that improvements in accuracy pay very high dividends, with a 10-kT weapon producing the same overpressure at 320 m as a 100-kT weapon produces at 688 m.

It is estimated that most human beings would perish and the majority of industrial structures would be destroyed by overpressures of 4.55 kg/m^2. An overpressure up to 21 kg/m^2 is produced at the edge of the fireball in a low-altitude explosion, and this pressure is assessed as being sufficient to rupture an arch of reinforced concrete buried under the ground, a structure similar to that which may be found to construct or protect command bunkers.

BLAST

Blast will take two forms: a fast-moving shock wave emanating away from the explosion, and a wind flow following the shock front (Fig. 4.4). The shock wave will travel fast initially, then will slow up. It will travel the first mile in about $2\frac{1}{2}$ sec, but may take up to $1\frac{1}{2}$ min to be felt at 20 miles. The pressure effect will be similar in pattern to that experienced from conventional high explosive; a sudden strong overpressure followed by an equally sudden fall back to ambient levels, followed by a longer but less intense fall below ambient before stabilising. A blow–suck–

blow effect (Fig. 4.5). The effect on target structures which cannot equalise the pressure changes rapidly (and most buildings cannot) will be to cause massive structural movement leading to extensive rupturing.

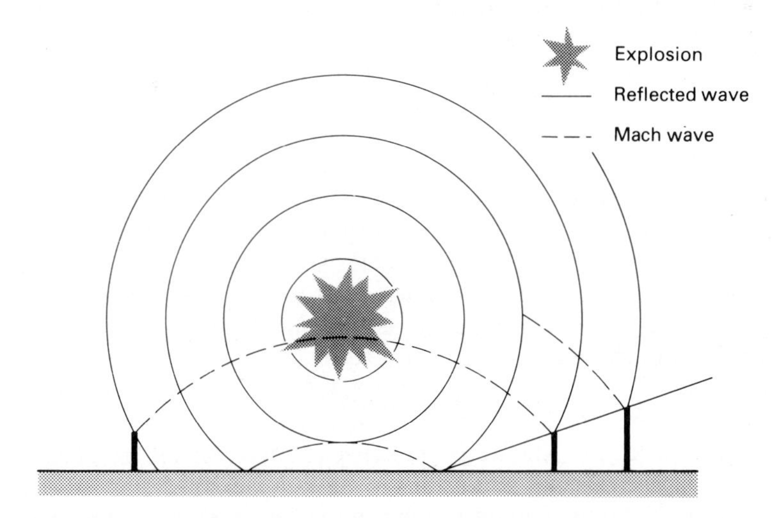

FIG. 4.4. Development of Mach waves.

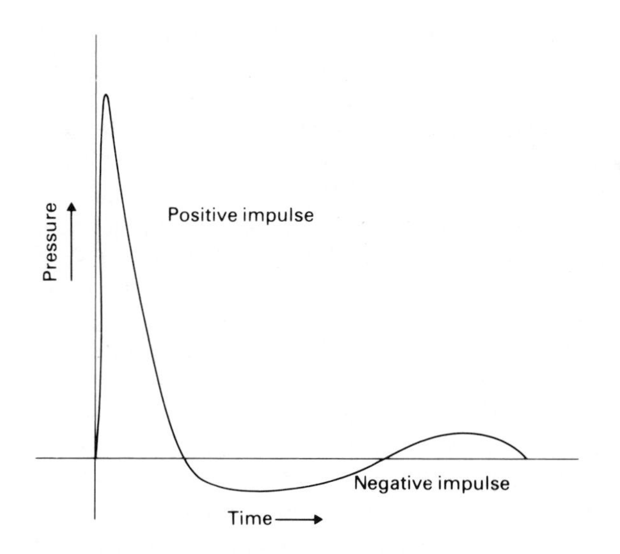

FIG. 4.5. Pressure against time for blast effect at any given point.

A similar effect is quite separately caused by the dynamic pressure, or the following wind, which trails the shock wave and is caused by the rush of air away from the detonation point. As this wind hits the structures in its path, it will also produce a blow–suck–blow effect, but this time of lower intensity but of longer duration. Video shots of targets at test ranges show well the influence of the two impacts, the shock wave and the following wind. Many structures will appear to jump slightly as the shock wave traverses them, a few small items may detach and the path of the shock wave can be seen travelling across sandy or dusty ground. The wind appears quite differently in a manner reminiscent of hurricane winds, and it is in this phase that windows are blown open and doors and roofs ripped away. The wind carries with it debris which in itself can be lethal. The wind speed can be very high—well over 1,000 mph close in to the ground zero, and peak dynamic pressures associated with such speeds can be over 80 lb/in^2.

The effect on specific targets is difficult to assess with any accuracy. Much will depend on the position of ground zero, the height of the burst and the yield of the weapon, all of which lend themselves to calculation, but the path of the shock wave and the following wind will be affected by terrain, the meteorological conditions, the altitude of the target area and the characteristics of the surface. In all a difficult task for the analyst, and one which will drive him towards caution in using a larger rather than a smaller warhead. Only as accuracy increases will his natural conservative approach be reversed.

THERMAL

The very intense heat of the fireball possesses in itself high thermal energy, but also transmits it as thermal radiations over a wide band varying from the ultraviolet to the infrared. The ultraviolet radiation tends to be absorbed by the atmosphere, leaving the other wavelengths as the prime source of the thermal radiation.

For an airburst weapon about a third of the total energy is released as thermal radiation (not heat in total which is much more). For every kiloton of energy released in an explosion, thermal energy is released equivalent to that from 400,000 1-kW electric fires; the time taken for this thermal energy to be radiated varies with the size of the weapon from under a $\frac{1}{2}$ sec for a 1-kT weapon to almost $\frac{1}{2}$ min for a weapon of 10-MT. It is also difficult to assess with any accuracy the effect on a target of thermal radiation. A host of factors influence it, including the state of the atmosphere at the time of the explosion and the thermal absorption qualities of the target. These include such things as colour, thickness, consistency and its reflective properties. This latter quality is important, and is the reason that the reflector of a radiant electric heater is silvered. Colour and reflectivity is a reason why the British 'V' bombers were painted with white gloss paint when they were used in the nuclear deterrent role. Reflection can in some circumstances enhance the effect of thermal radiation. When a weapon is detonated below an overcast, the underside of the cloud layer can act as a reflector and the reflected energy can be added to that coming direct from the point of the explosion.

The difficulty in planning the use of thermal effects as a damage mechanism is further complicated by the differing levels of energy release from the variously sized weapons. It is not only the amount of energy released which has an effect, but the rate at which it is released. In this, smaller weapons tend to release their thermal energy relatively quicker than larger weapons. The slower heat is generated, so the longer there is for it to be dissipated and conducted away. Consequently the amount of thermal energy required to produced second degree burns from a 1-MT weapon is over half as much again as required to produce the same effect from a 1-kT weapon. However, this level of energy, although much more, is still produced at very much greater ranges from the larger weapon; in the example a difference from 820 m from the 1-kT weapon to nearly 20,000 m from the 1-MT weapon.

Against some targets, the thermal effects can be very damaging. To a tank unit resting in a wood the blast and thermal effects together could prove devastating, with escape blocked by fallen trees and the whole wood set alight. Camouflage netting, tents, plastic sheeting, canvas vehicle tops will all be vulnerable to thermal effects at various ranges. The plastic insulation on power supply leads and aerial leads could all be affected by high thermal loads. From the human viewpoint, quite moderate protection can prove effective against high levels of thermal energy, providing that it is transitory. Earth is a particularly good protection, and a slit trench is an asset. Clothing can provide surprisingly effective relief, as can any shelter used to avoid direct exposure to the explosion. Simple experimentation can be done at home with a radiant electric heater. It soon proves that common sense applies.

The intense light which accompanies the nuclear explosion is a problem to the human eyes. Direct exposure to the flash of an explosion will cause 'flash blindness', which takes two forms. The first, and the most common, will be the dazzling effect of the intense light and will be similar to that experienced by camera flash bulbs or undipped car headlights at night. The difference is in intensity. Whereas the dazzle effect from a flash bulb will be a temporary inconvenience, that from a nuclear burst could be more prolonged and cause far greater loss of vision. Looking directly at a burst may result in severe impairment of vision for anything from 2–3 min by day to over 10 min at night, when the light will fall on eyes with the pupil fully dilated. Even 2 min can be a long time on a modern battlefield, and is even more so for pilots flying aircraft close to the ground at 8 nm/min.

The second and more serious form of 'flash blindness' is that which results from retinal burns received when the lens of the eyes focuses the image of the fireball onto the back of the eye. Estimates of the risk of retinal burns vary; some sources consider that only a few percent of troops will receive such injuries, others believe that this could be a more serious threat. Small pinpoint retinal burns may heal in time, but greater damage is unlikely to do so and will leave a permanent blind spot in the affected eye.

The development of the fireball has already been seen to be extremely fast, too fast to be countered by a natural blink. For some years devices have been sought to protect pilots from flash blindness. The best solution is to know where the explosion is to take place and to look away from the particular direction. Where strikes are preplanned a long way in advance, this can be built into briefings and route folders. Unfortunately flash blindness can equally be suffered from enemy strikes, and preknowledge of these is unlikely. The pilot could therefore be faced inadvertently with the blinding glare of an explosion in front of him.

A programme of research has been underway for many years, but until recently has not been particularly successful in developing any mechanical device to act sufficiently fast to block a nuclear flash. Mostly it was the inability of the mechanical devices to overcome inertia sufficiently quickly rather than any problem with the sensor which could work electronically. A breakthrough in this field may be in sight, with materials whose optical properties can be materially changed by passing current through them.

For the present the device used by strike pilots over the years still holds good—the eye-patch. A patch is worn over one eye and if a flash damages the uncovered eye the patch can be removed and the good eye used. The technique is not without its attendant dangers; those who have flown with an eye-patch for practice soon get concerned about depth perception. Man is a *bi*nocular animal. Gold-coated visors, or visors with a very fine layer of gold film between layers of acetate, have been used, but anything which lowers the total light transmissivity will not be welcome to pilots who must search for and locate small aircraft or ground targets without delay. The same objection arises over dark visors; to be effective against nuclear flash, they would have to be too dark to allow the pilot to fly safely at low level. Photochromatics, similar to that used in modern sunglasses, have been investigated and proved unsatisfactory on the grounds of slow operation. For the same reason photochromatic glasses can be dangerous if driving through road tunnels in bright conditions. Reducing the chance of receiving the flash by looking through a tunnel-vision viewing device is unsatisfactory for the same reason as before, the lack of vision which is so important to the pilot. In all, it remains a problem until some fast-acting visor can be developed which can obstruct the flash before it becomes dazzling. A similar problem is presented in defending against laser damage to the eye, and a solution to the two problems will probably be a common one.

NUCLEAR RADIATION

When a nuclear weapon is detonated, energy is released in the form of nuclear radiation. The most important of these radiations take the form of alpha particles, beta particles, gamma rays and neutrons.

Alpha particles have little penetrating power and are stopped by the lightest of materials. The danger occurs if material which is emitting alpha radiations gets access to the body internally. This may be through inhalation, digestion, or through wounds and abrasions. In this case considerable injury can be caused in time to the internal organs.

Beta particles also possess little penetrating power and will travel only a few metres in air. Within these constraints they could under certain circumstances penetrate the skin and could cause some skin burns, but compared to the other effects of the weapon this is not a major hazard. As beta particles are produced by the decay of fission products, they will form part of the residual nuclear radiation danger and are of more concern to decontamination parties than to aircrew.

Gamma rays are emitted from nuclear reactions and are a hazard both at the time of the explosion and subsequently. They are of shorter wavelength than X-rays, but resemble them in many other respects. They are extremely penetrative and can pass through many feet of the normal constructional materials and several inches of armour plate. It is for this reason that enhanced radiation weapons were to be fielded to counter the Soviet predominance in tanks. Gamma rays can travel very long distances in air and are particularly harmful to living organisms.

Neutrons, like gamma rays, are also highly penetrative and can travel long distances through the air. They are produced in quantity at the time of the explosion and present the greatest threat to living organisms during the initial radiation phase.

The damage to living tissue by nuclear radiation is caused by the ionisation and excitation of the cells which make up the tissue. Some essential components of the cells can be destroyed, damaged or changed in character. When the cell structure is damaged, it can in some circumstances produce poisons of its own. The ability of the body to accept nuclear radiation depends on the dose applied and whether only parts or the whole of the body was exposed. The areas of the body most sensitive to nuclear radiation are the bone marrow, spleen, gastrointestinal tract, the reproductive organs and the lymphoid tissue.

Of the 15 per cent or so of the total energy of the nuclear explosion released as radiation energy, about 5 per cent is released as initial energy and about 10 per cent as residual energy. Survival chances depend much on whether the exposure was as one dose or whether it was picked up over a long extended period. The body has some regeneration capability, and a small dose spread over a long period may not result in serious consequences.

The amount of radiation received will depend on several factors. The yield of the weapon is clearly important, but the relationship of radiation received is not linear with yield; higher-powered weapons deliver their radiation at a slower rate than smaller weapons (Fig. 4.6). The height of the burst affects the radiation received at any given point because the radiation has further to travel and distance is a factor acting similarly to its effect on thermal radiation; that is, the dose received is proportional to the square of the distance. Radiation is affected by absorption in the atmosphere, and consequently the lower the burst height, the greater the air density and the greater the absorption.

Using the measure of Roentgen Equivalent Mammal (rem), a unit of biological dose of radiation, an indication can be given to the effect on the human body. A dose of under 200 rem may give rise to some vomiting in a few hours from exposure, but the chance of death resulting is negligible. Under 600 rem the same vomiting may be experienced, but its onset time is shortened. It can also cause haemorrhaging and give rise to infection, and it is these last two causes which account for deaths in about 1 per cent of those exposed. Exposure to 1,000 rem gives all the problems outlined above, but in a more accute form, and very much higher death rates can be expected. Above 1,000 rem there is little chance of survival, and death rates may be between 90 and 100 per cent. Vomiting will be experienced very quickly, perhaps within $\frac{1}{2}$ hr and diarrhoea, fever, convulsions and tremor may be suffered. Death will take place between about 2 days and 2 weeks, dependent on dose.

A dose of 100 rem could be expected from a 1-kT burst at about $\frac{3}{4}$ mile and from a 10-MT weapon at 2.4 miles. 1,000 rem would be experienced from the same weapons at $\frac{1}{2}$ and 2 miles respectively.

DEBRIS FALLOUT

The combined effects of a nuclear burst at a near ground level will disturb or create a large amount of debris which is sucked up into the fireball and the

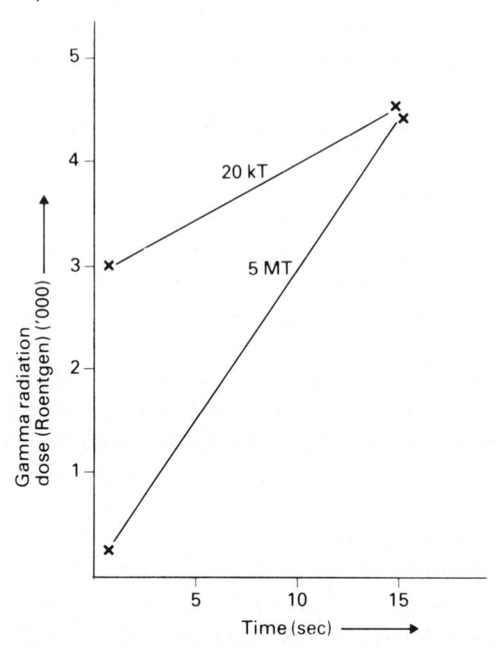

FIG. 4.6. Delivery of radiation from different yield weapons at a point $\frac{1}{2}$ mile from the explosion.

radioactive cloud where it becomes irradiated and mixed with the products of the explosion already there. Large particles will fall back to earth quickly, but much of the debris, some being little more than dust, will be carried to great heights by the hot rising cloud, and these will be carried by the generally strong upper winds for great distances. The only natural phenomenon which equates to this is the massive eruption of some volcanoes, when debris can be detected in the upper air currents thousands of miles away from the eruption. In this case the debris is not radioactive. The carriage of debris from an explosion for such long distances allows sampling of the atmosphere and from it a detailed analysis can enable the type and composition of the weapon to be determined. It also extends the reach of the fallout. It is difficult to predict fallout patterns accurately, as they are dependent on the rate of rise of the debris cloud, the strength and direction of the winds throughout the altitude covered and the rate at which the debris falls back to earth.

As the fallout descends on areas downwind of the explosion, so a degree of contamination is produced which can cause many of the physiological disorders explained previously. Accurate prediction, or prudent assumption, can allow protective measures to be taken in time to prevent combat casualties, but the operational penalty of operating in full Nuclear, Biological and Chemical (NBC) protective clothing with equipment which could be badly contaminated can be very heavy indeed. In this respect there is a strong similarity to the problems presented by nuclear fallout and persistent chemical agents.

What is the total effect of a nuclear airburst in a battlefield situation? For the sake of example consider a moderately sized tactical weapon, similar to the yield used against Japan, 20-kT.

The initial explosion will be noticeable from afar by the bright and intense light as the fireball develops in less than 'the twinkling of an eye'. Initially, the primary blast wave developing from the point of burst will not yet have reached the ground, but it will have been preceded by the thermal and radiation energy, both being transmitted at speeds initially close to that of light. A little over a second later the primary shock wave will have hit the ground and the reflected shock front will have started its development. About $\frac{1}{3}$ mile from ground zero there will be a start of the Mach reflection, where primary and reflected shock waves combine, and at this point the blast over pressure will be about 15 lb/in^2. At the 3-sec point the combined shock waves—the 'Mach front'—will be at a little under a mile from ground zero, the overpressure will have dropped to 6 lb/in^2, but it will now be followed by a dynamic wind blowing close to 200 mph, or about twice the speed experienced in hurricane-type winds. At the 10-sec point, the debris cloud will have formed in the familiar mushroom shape and is rising at the rate of about 200 mph. The Mach front has reached $2\frac{1}{2}$ miles and the overpressure has dropped to 1 lb/in^2 with a dynamic wind below 50 mph, but the influence of the hot fast-rising cloud above ground zero has caused the air now to be sucked after it up the mushroom stem causing a wind to flow strongly in towards ground zero and causing in turn more debris to be pulled into the air. At 30 sec the cloud is still rising at over 100 mph and winds blowing into and up the stem can be as high as 200 mph.

The effect nuclear weapons can have against targets can vary with a number of factors and is best summarised by a nomogram, one of many of which is shown in Fig. 4.7. Careful examination will show the importance of accuracy in reducing the need to use high-yield weapons. This nomogram refers to airburst weapons and to determine the effects from a surface burst the ranges obtained need to be multiplied by 0.75. It can also be determined that the area of destruction on the ground from ground zero increases at a factor of $Y^{\frac{2}{3}}$ where Y is the yield of the weapon, whereas the radius of destruction increases at the slower rate of $Y^{\frac{1}{3}}$. The radius of destruction is the more important parameter when calculating the effort required to engage a specific target.

The concept of multiple re-entry vehicles has allowed the weight of a given warhead to be more evenly distributed over a wide target area and against certain targets can greatly increase the effect of any given throw weight. As an example, the area of destruction of a 1-MT weapon against a large reinforced concrete building of blast-resistant design would be 1.4×10^7 m^2, whereas the area of destruction for the same total yield but delivered in the form of the 100-kT weapons would be 2.5×10^7 m^2 or, in round terms, nearly twice the area. Interestingly, conventional artillery is tending to move towards cluster or cassette rounds to optimise area coverage on much the same grounds, as air-carried cluster bombs such as the US Rockeye and the British BL755 have been designed for the same purpose.

The use of nuclear weapons on the battlefield is problematical. The necessity to obtain sufficient separation between friend and foe has already been rehearsed, but there are other considerations. These are more stringent for the attacker than

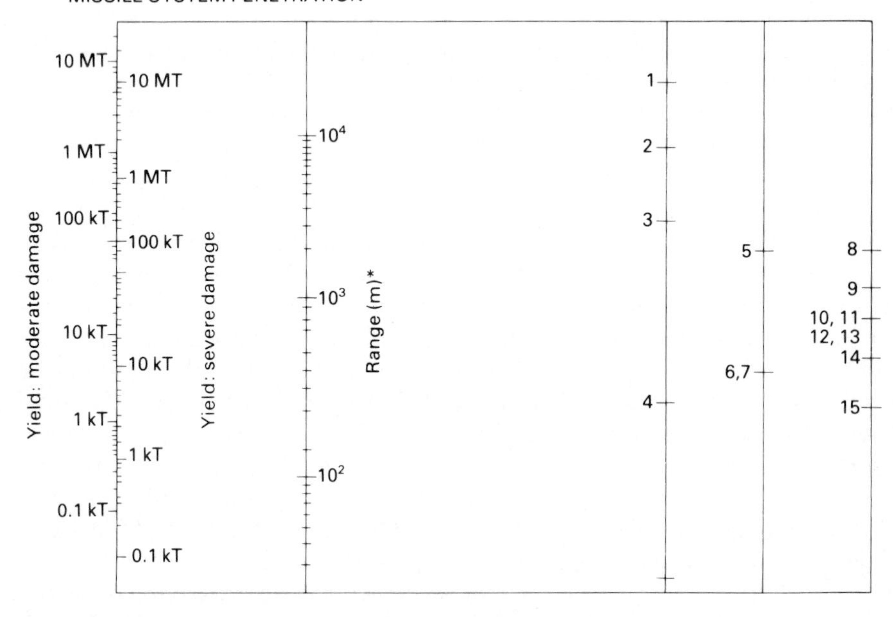

1. Wood-frame building.
2. Multistory, wall-bearing buildings, brick apartment house type.
3. Multistory, wall-bearing buildings, monumental type.
4. Multistory, blast-resistant design, reinforced-concrete buildings.
5. Multistory, reinforced-concrete buildings, with concrete walls and small window area.
6. Highway truss bridges of 45–75 m span (blast normal to longitudinal bridge axis).
7. Multistory, reinforced-concrete, frame office type buildings, earthquake resistant.
8. Light steel-frame industrial buildings.
9. Heavy steel-frame industrial buildings (25–50-ton crane).
10. Heavy steel-frame industrial buildings (60–100-ton crane).
11. Railroad truss bridges of 45–75 m span (blast normal to longitudinal bridge axis).
12. Multistory, reinforced-concrete frame office-type buildings.
13. Highway and railroad truss bridges of 75–120 m spans (blast normal to longitudinal bridge axis).
14. Multistory, steel-frame office type buildings.
15. Multistory, steel-frame office type buildings, earthquake resistant.

* For a surface burst multiply the range by three-quarters.

FIG. 4.7. Radius of damage of a nuclear blast for a number of types of structures.

the defender. It may not be advantageous to use a nuclear weapon against a strong defensive position if the result is to be heavy surface contamination which necessitates debilitating close-down operation NBC equipment. Or if blocked roads, fallen trees or extensive fires are going to slow the advance of armour and supporting vehicles so that the advantage confirmed by the destruction of the enemy cannot be exploited before he can reinforce or regroup. It is also of little value if the prevailing wind deposits radioactive fallout on follow-up friendly troops, so exhausting them before the battle is joined.

The further the potential nuclear target is away from the immediate contact battle, the easier it is to contemplate the use of nuclear weapons. Airfields, particularly those supporting nuclear-capable units, storage and assembly areas and communications choke points, could all be lucrative targets under the right circumstances.

Nuclear attack is an economical attack; a single aircraft or missile can create the same damage as squadrons of aircraft using conventional weapons. In this way nuclear defence is cheap compared with any conventional force even approaching equivalence in effect, but in this area technology is starting to offer weapons which would blur the previously clear differentiation between conventional and nuclear weapons.

For some time there has been a movement towards miniaturisation of nuclear weapons and towards sub-kiloton yields. Artillery can fire nuclear rounds, and this NATO capability is balanced by similar capability in the Warsaw Pact. But the difference in effect on the target between a small yield nuclear round and a cluster of modern fuel-air or reactive-surround conventional warheads may be difficult to determine. The great gap in effect which used to exist between conventional and nuclear weapons, which made the escalatory step between the two so large and clear, now exists perhaps more in emotional than in physical terms. Would the release of such a small yield weapon, with conceivably less effect than conventional attacks already absorbed, be the cause for an escalatory response? If not, would the next one? If not, which one would justify the escalation and at what level? The problem was in many respects easier to rationalise in those early nuclear times when there was little doubt that an initial attack on Brussels or Birmingham could be countered by a retaliatory strike against Omsk or Tomsk.

From the strike pilot's viewpoint, the techniques involved in the delivery of a nuclear weapon are very similar to those involved in conventional operations apart from the measures taken to protect against flash blindness already outlined. In some respects the nuclear load is an asset. Nuclear weapons, other than the very high yields unlikely to be delivered by attack aircraft, are relatively small and light. Consequently there is less drag, allowing higher penetration speeds and greater radius of action, and the increased weight margin can allow more drop tanks to be carried, so increasing range even further. Although 'Kamikaze' operations are not a normal feature of Western air operations, there is always the possibility of extending strike range by accepting one-way missions where the aircraft could head for neutral territory after a target strike or even fly to a selected abandonment area. Deep strike is, however, much better left to ballistic missile or cruise missile attack.

The question was posed as to whether the nuclear weapon was something different, or was it merely a bigger and better bang. It is different and it deserves to be treated so not only because its very 'bigness' is of such orders of magnitude greater than conventional weapons that it really is in another class, but because the radiation and fallout implications put quite new and massive complications into any comparative assessment.

It is a weapon which took the world by surprise in 1945, and appeared on the scene with an impact rarely achieved by the most talented impressario. It arrived in the human experience well ahead of general human understanding or education on matters nuclear, and many have still to reconcile themselves with the emotional shock it so caused. This is a pity because the debate on the subject ofttimes lacks the subjectivity which it fully deserves, and there are those who argue their corner, both corners, to the exclusion of the wider scene which is, in many areas, presenting equal if not greater menace.

Whether the human race should concern itself so much with the nuclear issue when a balance, even a 'balance of terror', exists to preserve the peace, when far more awful threats such as the advanced chemical or even biological threats remain unbalanced, is a very debatable point.

PLATE 3.1. A Jaguar of 20 Squadron showing what external stores can do to sleek high-speed aircraft. Here the aircraft is loaded with, from left to right: an electronic warfare pod, a 1,000-lb bomb with Paveway laser-guidance equipment fitted, a fuel tank at centre-line, another laser-guided bomb, and a chaff dispenser pod. Although the outboard pods reduce the bomb load, the increased accuracy possible from the 'smart' bombs does much to compensate for the smaller load. (Crown copyright.)

PLATE 3.2. The Tornado, seen here in its strike/attack version, together with the air defence variant, will form the backbone of the RAF into the twenty-first century.

PLATE 3.3. A Jaguar showing the two AIM-9 air-to-air missiles which makes it a difficult target for air defence fighters when they approach it from height in an attempt to stop the very low-level penetration. The opportunity shot against Combat Air Patrol aircraft is always a possibility. (RAF.)

PLATE 3.4. Two F-4 Phantoms take-off over a row of Buccaneers at Exercise Red Flag. In the clear Nevada air the smoky exhausts are evident. This is a major disadvantage in combat and US specifications since the late sixties have called for smoke-free engines. (Author.)

PLATE 3.5. The Vulcan bomber, mainstay of the deterrent force, now withdrawn from service. Its range as a so-called 'strategic' bomber can now be equalled by much smaller aircraft utilising air-to-air refuelling. (RAF.)

PLATE 3.6. Although an old aircraft, the Buccaneer, with its long-range and low-drag internal weapon carriage, can still out-speed and out-distance much more modern aircraft. It was designed for the maritime role and with improved avionics is still a force to be reckoned with. With air-to-air refuelling its range can closely match that of the earlier Vulcan Bombers. (RAF.)

PLATE 3.7. It is not only weapons which cause high drag but also the suspension equipment. Here a US triple ejection rack is seen on the pylon of an F-4 Phantom. (Author.)

PLATE 4.1. The Buccaneer is an old aircraft by today's standards, but it can still outperform many aircraft of the modern era. Part of its success lies in its internal bomb bay which overcomes the external drag penalty of bomb carriage. It also allows pylon space to be used for defensive purposes; this 15 Squadron aircraft has electronic warning pods to port and an IR AIM-9 Sidewinder air-to-air missile to starboard. (Crown copyright.)

5

Weapons

In the combat roles the aircraft is merely the intermediary step in the achievement of the aim; it is the weapon which engages the target. The importance placed by the British upon weapons varies between peace and war, historically tending to place too little emphasis on them during peace and having to take extraordinary measures when faced with the reality of war.

Admiral Hipper, speaking of the Battle of Jutland, said that, 'it was nothing but the poor quality of the British bursting charges that saved us from disaster'. In the same battle, one of his opponents, Admiral Beatty, exclaimed 'what's wrong with our bloody ships today?' as the German shells proved that their operational test and evaluation had been conducted more thoroughly than had that of the British.

It took World War II to inspire the development of new aircraft bombs after those available at the start of war were proved to be ineffective. Some innovative designs saw service and the Tallboy bombs and the bouncing bomb developed specially for the dam-busting raids were most notable. The 1,000 lb bomb, designed it is said to fulfil the internal carriage requirements of the Lancaster bomber in the early 1940s, is still being carried on RAF front-line aircraft 40 years later, and is likely to see service into the twenty-first century. The shape remains unchanged despite now being carried externally on aircraft designed for high-speed flight. The contradiction is self-evident.

In 1968, when the first hardened-aircraft-shelter (HAS) appeared and started the trend towards hardening airfields and so protecting the primary target, the aircraft, a move was made towards attacking the operating surfaces as a method of preventing operations. Only in the mid-eighties are weapons starting to see service, such as the German MW-1, the British JP233 and the French Durandel, designed to match the particular characteristics of the target. In the Falklands conflict, two American weapons, the Harpoon and the Shrike, had to be procured in haste to meet the threat from a Third World opponent and this by a nation poised daily to resist aggression from the world's most aggressively militaristic power. Another seeming contradiction, but pointing to the traditional British reserve about weapon development.

The development of explosives is closely related to advances in chemistry and the chemical industry. Before 1800 the field was small, consisting mainly of gunpowder which was used for blasting and as a propellant, but the discovery of mercury fulminate at the turn of the century marked a change in the pace of progress and in the nineteenth century both nitrocellulose and nitroglycerine entered the market. Towards the end of that century a series of other substances emerged as by-product of the gas and coke ovens and from the dye industry which, when compounded with nitric acid, produced the basis for many modern explosives; benzene, toluene, naphthalene and phenol for example.

Explosives exist in two forms: *low* explosives, which explode slowly, that is from milliseconds to seconds, generally used as propellants and are normally referred to that way, and *high* explosives, which explode in microseconds and are used to produce the destructive effects normally associated with bombs and warheads.

The effect of a high explosive is to shatter things in its immediate vicinity, and its capability to do this, known as its *Briance*, depends on the ability to produce large amounts of energy in the form of heat and of gas, and to complete the process quickly. The release of heat alone will produce an explosive effect as the air in the immediate vicinity expands, but a much greater effect is obtained if the explosive itself generates large amounts of gas. Most explosives do so, normally gaseous variants of carbon, hydrogen, oxygen and nitrogen.

The effectiveness of a high explosive depends upon the speed at which the chemical change occurs. This is referred to as the *Velocity of Detonation (VOD)* and is affected by three factors: the density at which the explosive medium is packed, the dimension of the charge and the degree in which the charge is confined. If the charge is densely packed, the shock wave of detonation can pass between the individual crystals of the mixture better and therefore faster than if they were further apart, as in the case of a less-dense packing. Experimentation has shown that the VOD is influenced by the diameter of the charge and falls off markedly below certain diameters. A similar picture emerges for confinement, and the VOD falls sharply when a bomb or shell casing reduces below a certain thickness. In the extreme form, when there is no casing and the mixture lies unconfined, it will sometimes burn rather than explode.

The main filling of a weapon needs to be both reasonably insensitive and, to allow reasonable shelf-life, it needs to be chemically stable. Together, these qualities can result in some reluctance to detonate and it is customary to use an explosive chain to initiate detonation. Usually this is a three-part process consisting of the main filling, an intermediary filling of about half the insensitivity of the main filling, and an initiator which is about half the insensitivity of the intermediary.

In aircraft bombs the main fillings are generally RDX or TNT, and these mixtures feature in combination in a variety of military weapons such as mines, depth charges, torpedos and guided-weapon warheads. RDX has a high VOD, as does HMX, and as the penetration of a shaped-charge jet is proportional to the square of the VOD these mixtures feature largely in such weapons.

When detonation occurs, pressures of many thousands of pounds per square inch (lb/in^2) are generated and the casing of the weapon fractures, allowing the expanding gases to escape at a speed initially close to the VOD. The force of such high-speed gas has a directly destructive effect on anything in its path, but the turbulence caused by gas travelling at speeds approaching 20,000 mph adds to the overall effect. The blast effect takes the form of a high initial overpressure, followed rapidly by a less intense by nonetheless significant underpressure, before the pressure reverts to the normal. It is this 'blow-and-suck' effect which can be so destructive to targets, particularly those which cannot equalise the pressure. A wall of a warehouse, for example, would be particularly bad at accepting the pressure wave from a high explosive, but the supporting cables of a suspension bridge would allow a high measure of pressure equalisation. Both structures can be damaged by a high explosive, but the range at which the damage was caused would be much greater in the case of the warehouse given an equal charge weight.

A further effect of the high-explosive device derives from the fragmentation of the casing. The air blast from an explosion soon dissipates and may have lost much of its destructive power outside some 50 ft or so from the explosion. The fragments of casing, however, will have picked up very high-energy levels and will carry considerable distances beyond that of the air blast.

If the purpose of the case is only to contain the explosive mixture, the fragment size will be random, varying from very large to very small sizes. Conversely, if the bomb has been designed to optimise the fragmentation effect, the case may be prescored to provide weak points or constructed in other ways, such as wire-wrapping, to ensure uniform and predictable fragmentation. The velocity of the fragments will relate to the relationship between charge weight and the mass and construction of the casing. Thin-walled weapons, where the primary purpose may be the blast effect from high charge weights, may produce small fragments travelling at speeds as high as 11,000 ft/sec. General purpose bombs will provide heavier fragments moving at up to 9,000 ft/sec and specialist fragmentation weapons will produce heavier fragments which travel at up to 5,000 ft/sec.

The mass of the fragment determines how fast it loses its energy as it travels through the air. A five-grain fragment travelling at 6,000 ft/sec will lose half its velocity in 37 ft, while a 500-grain fragment would travel 175 ft before experiencing the same decay. There seems to be a clear advantage to using heavier fragments, but this is tempered by the chances of obtaining a hit on the target. There will be fewer fragments of high mass and the density of fragments in any given direction varies inversely as the distance from the weapon. In the extreme, if only two fragments were produced, say the casing split in half, then the fragment path might be very long in two directions, but in all other directions there would be no fragmentation effect. Conversely, if the casing fractured into 10,000 small fragments, the angular cover about the bomb would probably be comprehensive, but only to a relatively small range due to the low mass of the individual fragments (Fig. 5.1).

The distribution of fragments depends on a number of factors other than the size and velocity. The pattern tends to be out to the side of the bomb normal to the longitudinal axis, that is, if the bomb was standing on its nose the fragments would tend to fly out parallel to the surface. This generalisation is modified somewhat by other circumstances. For example, the fragments will assume a component equal to the velocity of the bomb, so that for a bomb dropping vertically and detonating before ground impact there will be both a vertical component due to the bomb velocity and a horizontal velocity due to the forces of the detonation. A pattern resembling an inverted saucer would result. If the bomb was flying at an angle, the distribution would be skewed because those fragments being ejected upwards would lose energy faster than those ejected downwards. Fuzing also has an effect. If the fuze is in the tail, the detonation will start in the tail and move forward. Even though this delay is very small, it is enough to affect the fragmentation pattern

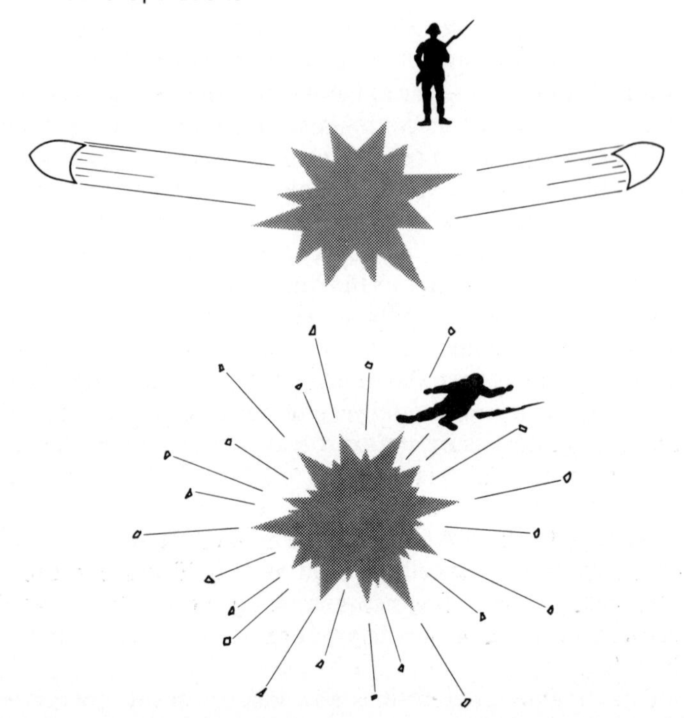

FIG. 5.1. Fragmentation. Small fragments tend to lose their velocity quicker than large fragments. The case designer can either opt for comprehensive but short-range cover, or extend the range by using large fragments but reduce the probability of a target strike.

slightly; a tail fuzing skews the pattern forward and a nose fuzing skews the pattern to the rear.

Just as the effect of an explosion is enhanced if it is confined within the casing, so is the effect of the weapon as a whole enhanced if it explodes within a target rather than outside or on the surface. It is for this reason that penetration is important, and this is affected by the characteristics of the bomb casing and the velocity at which it impacts. If the bomb impacts a hard target at too high a speed, the casing can fracture, so leaving the explosive mixture unconfined with the possibility of a 'burn' rather than an explosion or even a complete dud. Bombs designed for penetration of hard targets are characterised by high casing weights in relation to charge weights. A small amount of explosive in a confined space can cause considerable damage and the advantages are considerable of good penetration qualities and reliable fuzes, designed to detonate the bomb after penetration has been achieved.

There are many variables which affect penetration other than casing strength and impact velocity. Nose shape affects the path of the bomb through plastic substances such as earth or clay, as does the composition of the target material. There are many types of soil and clay, each with marked differences, as there is with concrete, the material used to construct a variety of militarily attractive targets. The concrete strength, and the aggregate size and type, materially affect the degree of penetration achieved, as does the amount of steel reinforcement used; in normal structural concrete this amounts to between 2 per cent and 4 per cent by volume.

A typical medium-capacity bomb may be limited to an impact velocity against a massive concrete structure of about 750 ft/sec if the casing is to remain intact. Dropped against concrete with a compressive strength of 5,000 lb/in^2 the maximum thickness of concrete likely to be breached is only in the order of 2 ft.

The degree of penetration depends on the thickness of the concrete. If the concrete is very thick, the bomb will embed in it and there will be no breaching. If the concrete is thinner, the point will be reached when the shock wave which travels ahead of the nose as it penetrates reaches the other side of the slab and detaches concrete from the inside face. This is known as spalling. As the slab reduces in thickness, the loss of the spall from the inner face effectively weakens the concrete in the path of the bomb and it can travel further before it is arrested. Finally, when the slab thickness reduces further, the bomb penetrates through to the spall area and complete penetration is achieved (Fig. 5.2).

The depth of penetration in plastic substances is also affected by nose shape and the mass characteristics of the bomb. If the bomb impacts at less than 90° to the plane of the target, there will be a tendency for the weapon to arc towards the surface, causing the bomb to follow a curved path underground. In the extreme case, the bomb can even broach the surface some distance away from a low-angle impact point, negating any desired cratering effect (Fig. 5.3).

Cratering is important against a variety of targets, particularly runways, roads and railways. If penetration is shallow, a matter of a few feet, a large crater will result, but one which has the loose debris resting on sound subsoil. As penetration depth increases, so the more an underground cavity is formed, a *camouflet*, and this requires extensive excavation to find sound subsoil before compacted fill and repair can take place. Without this troublesome procedure, the bearing strength of the repaired surface cannot be properly restored (Fig. 5.4).

It can be seen that to obtain the best penetration an impact at high speed is required as near to normal to the surface as can be obtained. Typically, high-level bombing achieves this with bombs reaching near terminal velocity and falling close to the vertical. Since the effectiveness of air defences have forced aircraft to attack lower, it has been progressively more difficult to achieve these parameters. If a bomb is dropped at low level, the time of flight will be only a few seconds, and if the bomb is not retarded to fall behind the aircraft, the resulting explosion would destroy the aircraft. But in achieving the retardation the velocity of the bomb is severely reduced so affecting its penetrability. For example, a bomb released at 500 kts (845 ft/sec) at 150-ft release altitude will be in the air only 3.4 sec, during which time it will be retarded to an impact velocity of 328 ft/sec, reducing the penetration capability against anything but relatively soft targets.

Low-level retarded bombing also presents other problems. The bomb in the example would impact at a little over 12°, yet impact angles of greater than 20° are required if ricochet is not to result from soft surfaces such as water or earth. Angles in excess of 40° are required if ricochet is to be avoided from hard surfaces such as concrete. Prudent weaponeers usually attempt to better these figures. If a bomb is likely to ricochet due to the low impact angle resulting from a low angle delivery,

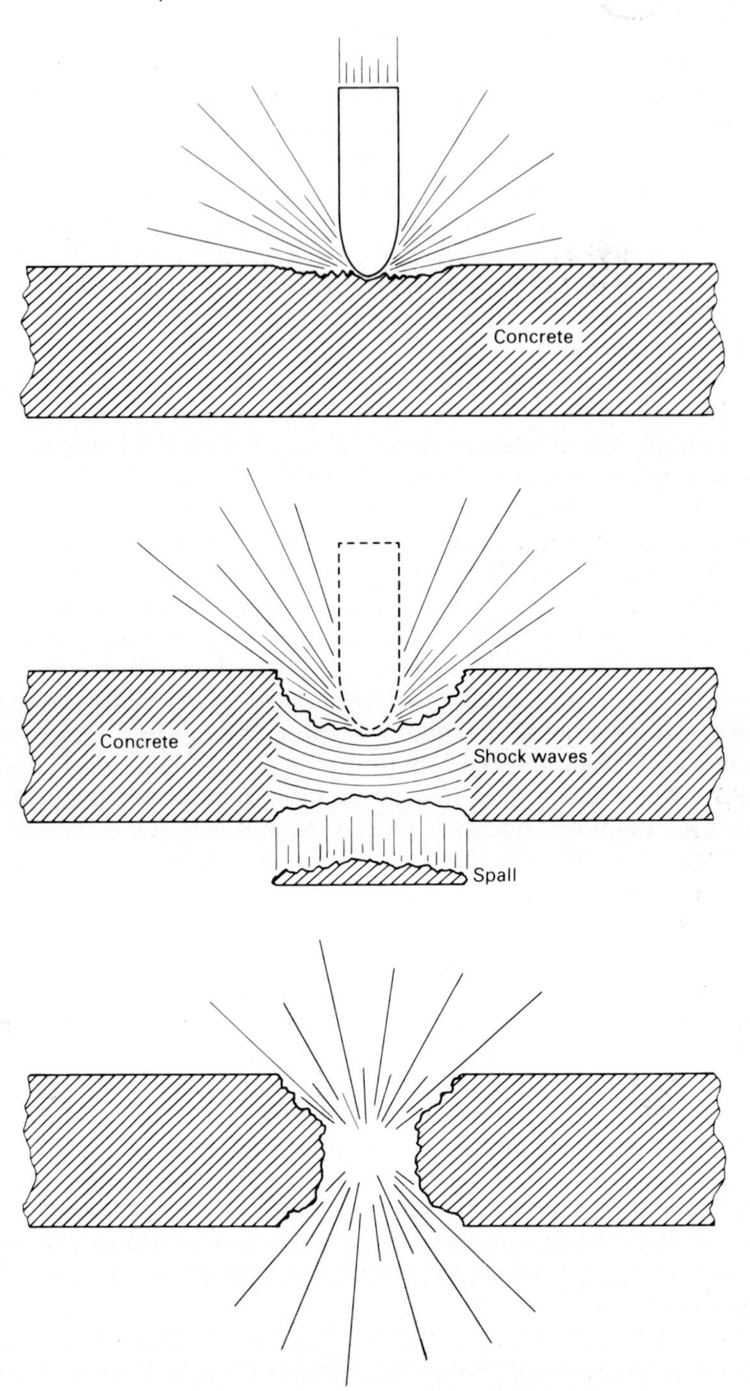

FIG. 5.2. The three stages of penetration. The effectiveness of the bomb in penetration will depend on the quality of the concrete, the strength of the bomb casing, its shape, the filling and the angle of impact.

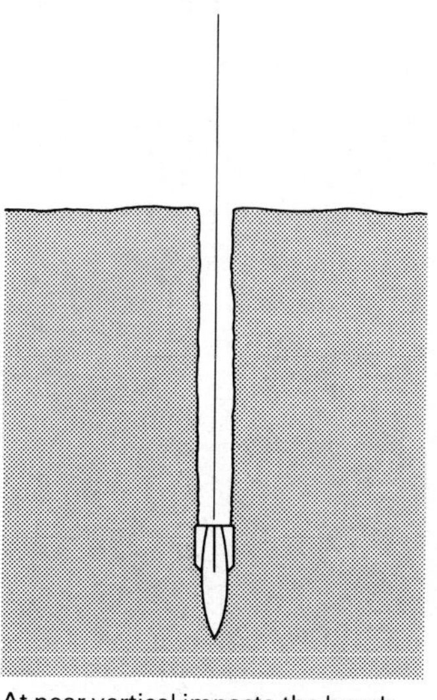

At near vertical impacts the bomb embeds close to the vertical.

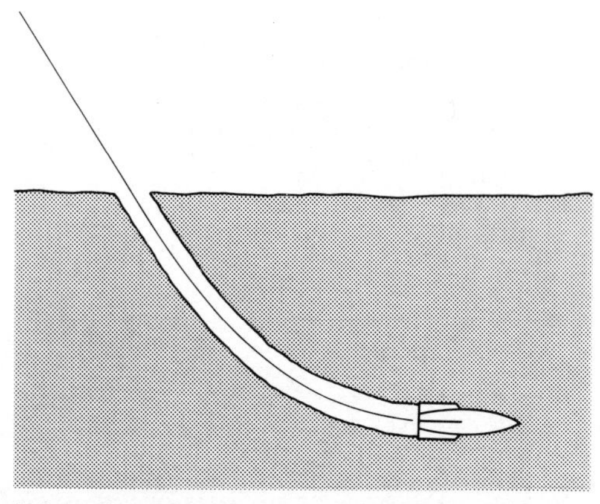

At lower impact angles the bomb tends to arc towards the horizontal and at very shallow angles can even breach the surface some way away. The phenomenon complicates the task of bomb disposal – first find the bomb – but can be used to effect against ships.

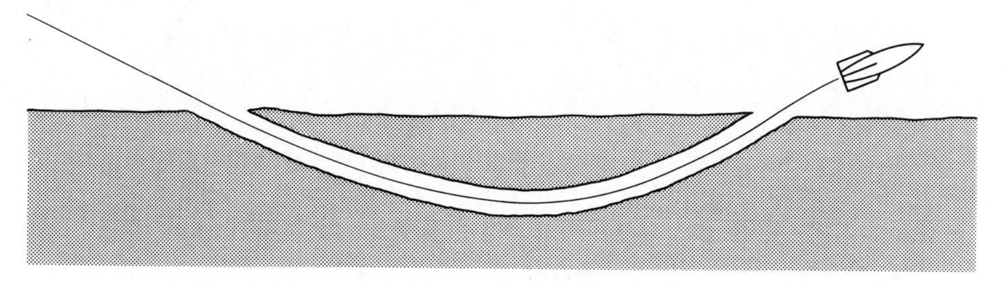

FIG. 5.3. Bomb behaviour at varying impact angles striking plastic substances.

the fuzing must be made instantaneous to ensure that the bomb detonates adjacent to the target, and such fuzing effectively prevents penetration in any event. There can be, therefore, a high penalty in weapon effectiveness for being forced to operate at low level for survival against air defences.

A method used to get the required impact velocity and angle but retaining the low-level approach to the target is the loft attack in which the aircraft releases ballistic, or unretarded, bombs from the early stages of a looping manoeuvre, so *tossing* or *lofting* the bombs onto the target. The accuracy of this attack is invariably less than the very accurate laydown method and depends greatly on the skill of the crew and the effectiveness of the weapon system. Earlier aircraft could expect loft accuracies to be six or seven times worse than typical laydown accuracies; more modern systems can reduce this to a factor of 3 or 4. Against large area targets this may still suffice, as it may against high value targets such as major naval surface combatants where, although the probability of hit is low, the almost sure kill resulting from an embedded 1,000-lb detonation may make the attack highly cost-effective.

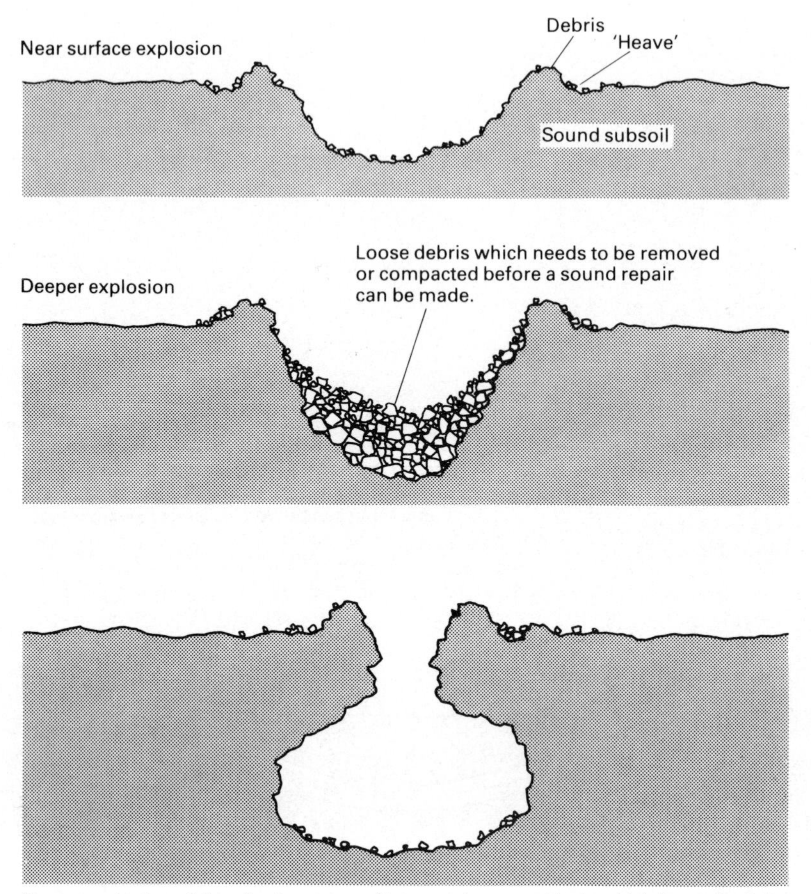

FIG. 5.4. Cratering.

FUEL-AIR EXPLOSIVES (FAE)

It has been seen so far that to obtain the best effect from a high explosive it is necessary to confine it, normally by use of a bomb casing, but even after impact it is advantageous if target penetration can be obtained to enhance further the explosive effect. This is as true with high explosives as it is with low explosives, or propellants, which are also optimised by confinement, by a shell case, a gun barrel or, even in the case of a rocket motor, by the nozzle arrangements. A type of weapon operating on what seems to be a quite opposite principle is becoming more popular. These are the fuel-air explosives.

While the principle of fuel-air explosives had been known about for some time, the incentive to develop them apace came in Vietnam where two particular problems faced the US forces. The first was the skill of the Vietcong in using underground accommodation, in some instances extending for many miles and containing domestic and administrative accommodation, the latter extending to hospitals where primitive but major surgery was performed. A layer of earth only a few feet thick was sufficient to insulate the occupants from the fragmentation effects of bombs and from the blast effects of anything but a penetrating bomb. Even penetrating bombs had little total area of effect, a factor magnified by the situation normally existing at the time, which was uncertainty of the exact location of the tunnels.

The second reason emerged from the highly wooded nature of the terrain. The helicopter was used extensively in South-East Asia and in many areas took the place of a conventional truck, but helicopter operations are greatly impaired by forest, it being difficult, and at times impossible, to lower or hoist some loads through the forest top. The clearance of suitably sized helicopter sites in the dense forest could prove time-consuming and a method was sought to make such sites by use of air dropped bombs. Conventional bombs proved inefficient, too much of their explosive effect was used to produce fragmentation which was not effective and it was difficult to drop sufficient bombs on the same point to produce the required clearing.

The fuel-air explosive works by containing within a light casing an explosive 'fuel'. At a distance above the surface the weapon initiates and the mixture is distributed widely in a fine mist, so mixing with the 'air'. After an appropriate delay to permit proper distribution and mixing, the charge is initiated. The result is an explosion producing a major shock effect over a very wide area (Fig. 5.5).

The effectiveness of fuel-air weapons against tunnels is not common knowledge, but it can be supposed that unless the mixture penetrated into the tunnels the effect would not have been very great. Had it done so the effect in the confined area of the tunnels could have been dramatic. Against dense forest the effect was well documented and FAE proved to be an excellent medium for constructing helicopter landing sites.

There are a number of problems to overcome in the design and use of FAE devices. The fuel-air mixture to obtain optimal effect is critical, and it is not an easy task to arrange for the mixture to be consistent over the wide area. The time taken to complete the distribution and the point when ignition is initiated is again critical; too soon and the mix may be too rich and the area covered too small; too late and the cloud of mixture could be adversely affected by strong winds or other weather effects. It was the difficulty in solving these largely mechanical problems that caused development of FAE weapons to be slower than many expected given the promise of the theory.

The large area of intense shock effect makes FAE weapons suitable for use against a variety of military targets, including bunkers, hardened-aircraft shelters, and any soft-skinned targets in the open or in shallow revetments. This latter group also includes aircraft, large or small, standing in the open. FAE can also prove to be effective against targets such as bridges, where the large-area shock wave can impact greater energy into the structure than is possible from the more intense point source of the more conventional bomb.

The large destructive effect of FAE is produced from weapons proportionally smaller than conventional bombs. This points to their use as warheads on vehicles where either weight or size is critical. Cruise missiles may prove to be an application for the technology. There must be a minimum size below which there

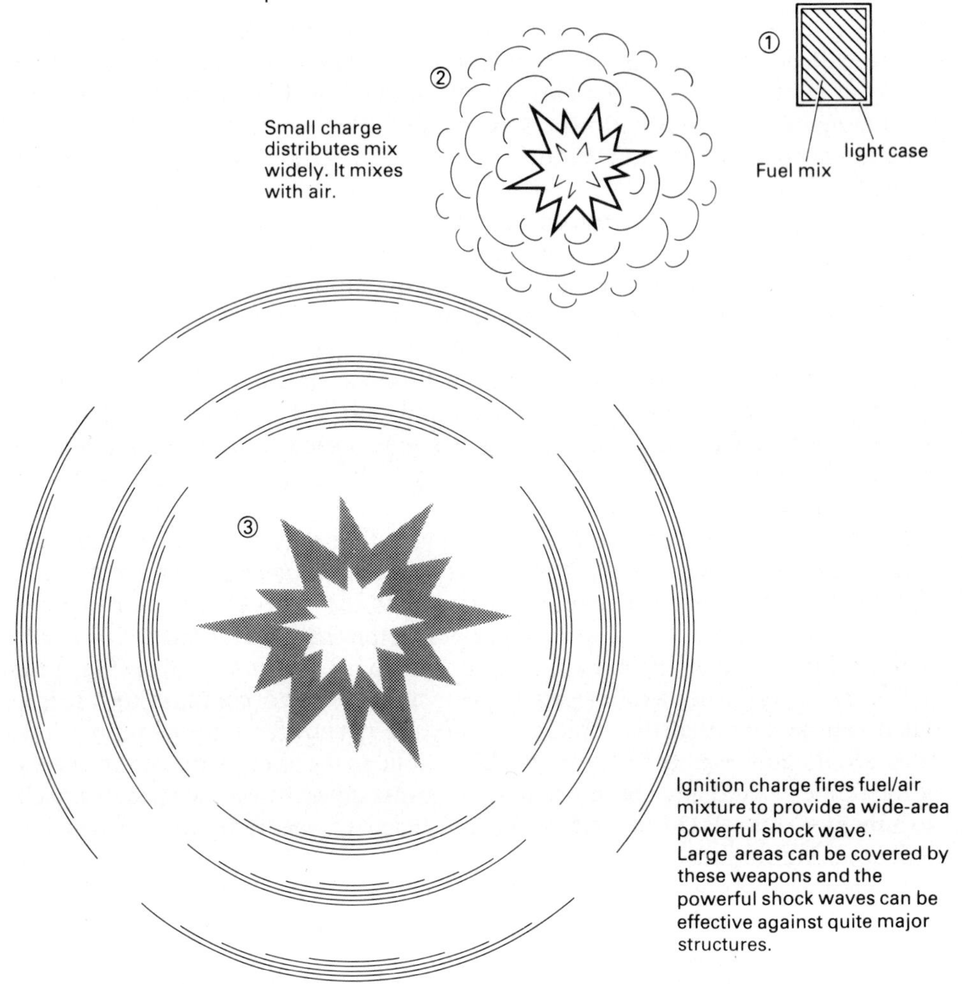

FIG. 5.5. Fuel-air weapons.

would be little advantage over using conventional explosive; FAE essentially requires a large area distribution for maximum effect. It could also prove difficult to disperse the vapour cloud efficiently from very-high-speed delivery vehicles. The use of FAE in ballistic missile heads would therefore be problematical unless the re-entry vehicle was artificially decelerated before warhead initiation.

If used in warheads of a reasonable size, however, FAE can produce effects which have been described by some, including some Soviet commentators, as approaching those of tactical nuclear weapons, but in a more controllable and localised manner. FAE may prove to be the natural choice of weapon whenever blast damage is required without penetration.

HOLLOW-CHARGE WEAPONS

Hollow-charge weapons, sometimes referred to more descriptively as shaped-charge, are used primarily against armour. When activated, the charge is detonated from the rear and the shock wave travels forward, collapsing a shaped metal liner towards the axis and forming a narrow high-velocity jet of gas which possesses high energy. This jet can penetrate considerable thicknesses of armour plate. To obtain the optimum effect, a hollow-charge weapon must detonate some distance from the target; this stand-off distance depends upon the particular characteristics of the weapon and its fuzing, but generally lies between three and eight times the diameter of the charge (Fig. 5.6).

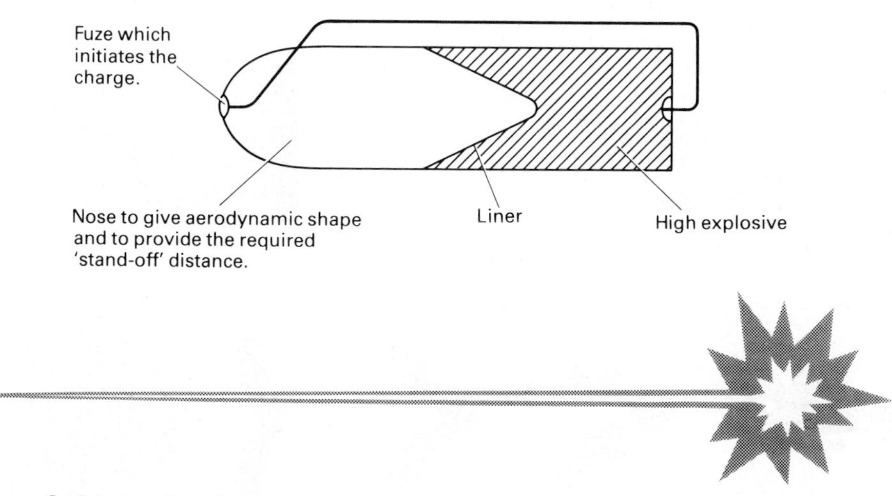

FIG. 5.6. Hollow-charge warheads.

The angle at which the weapon strikes the target is important. As with bombs, the maximum penetration is achieved if the jet strikes the armour at right angles. A hollow-charge weapon of 2-in diameter, whose shaped liner encompasses a 50° angle, would penetrate just over 4 in of rolled homogeneous armour (RHA), used as a standard in such measurements, or about 4.6 in of mild steel. However, if the weapon impacted the target 50° off the perpendicular, the penetrations would be reduced to 2.7 in and a little under 3 in respectively.

The hollow-charge principle has been used in aircraft-launched rocket projectiles such as the SNEB 68 mm, the US 2.75 in and the 80 mm SURA. The hollow-charge weapon relies upon chemical energy for its effect and is therefore not demanding in terms of velocity, although this can have an effect on obtaining the hit in the first instance. Because of this, the diameter of the round need not be unnecessarily constrained, and if used in weapons such as the Multi-Launch Rocket System (MLRS) or dispersed from pods or bus vehicles the diameters of submunitions can be made quite large. This is one method in which the weapon designer can keep pace, or even overtake, his tank designer colleague who has recently been making major advances in tank armour effectiveness.

FORGED-FRAGMENT WEAPONS

Of increasing interest is the forged-fragment weapon. It owes something to the hollow-charge principle in that the basic explosive mechanism is similar, but where in the case of the hollow-charge the energy is concentrated in a high-velocity gas jet, in the forged-fragment weapon the energy is concentrated on a more substantial liner which is 'forged' by the concentrated shock waves into a projectile which is then directed at the target. The technique is still in the formative stage, but promises much in the future if sensor technology and aiming problems can be overcome (Fig. 5.7).

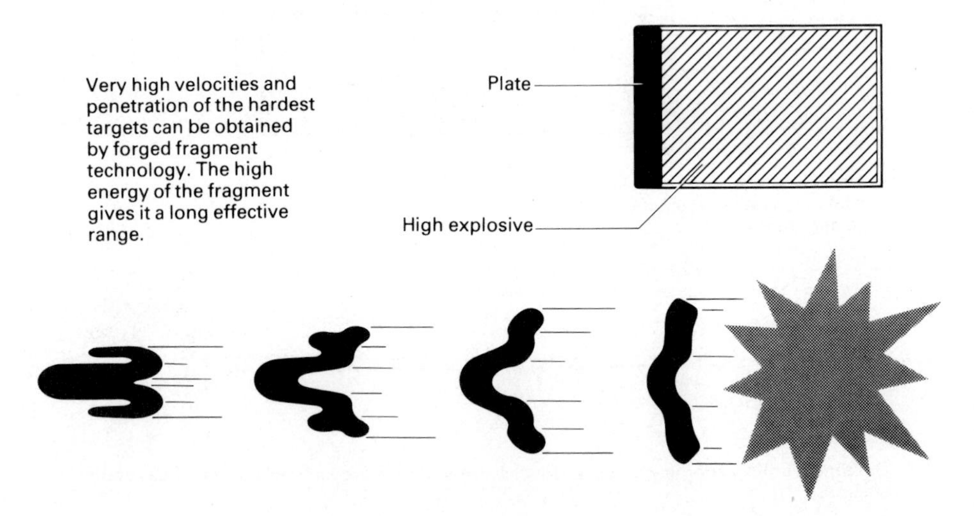

FIG. 5.7. Forged fragment.

KINETIC ENERGY

Kinetic energy (KE) effects are those most readily understood. It is the application of superior force, or 'brute strength', and is typified by MV^2. Although there is some application of kinetic energy weapons to aircraft use in such systems as the US GAU-8 gun in the Fairchild A-10, or in the Canadian RPV-7 rocket, the technique is more widely used in ground-based systems such as tank guns. This may change in the future, as research into hypersonic rockets bears fruit. Currently, the penalty for airborne use can be high. The GAU-8 gun requires an aircraft the size of the A-10 to carry it. Dismounted, the whole assembly is the same size as a Volkswagen Beetle and the recoil forces from such a weapon are difficult to contain conveniently in an aircraft structure designed with weight reduction much in mind. Obtaining high velocities from rockets also tends to require large-diameter, and therefore high-drag rocket motors, or long-burn motors which result in long-range firings, with all the accuracy and target-acquisition problems which that implies.

In kinetic energy weapons the balance between mass and velocity is important. The velocity factor is squared, and consequently the greatest immediate improvement is to be found in a velocity increase. Modern tank guns are capable of achieving muzzle velocities around 1,600 m/sec and 1,800 m/sec is thought to be possible from the increasingly common smooth-bore guns. Tank guns tend to be of large calibre, 105 mm and 120 mm being popular sizes, and the frontal area of such a round would cause high aerodynamic drag which would soon decay the velocity. The answer has been the discarding sabot, a device encasing a fine round, enlarging it to fill the bore of the gun and on which the force of the gun pressure can be exerted. On exit from the barrel, the sabot breaks away, leaving the low-drag penetrator to proceed. To achieve a high mass despite the small frontal area, the penetrator has to be long and thin and a ratio of 1:20 is thought to be about the maximum possible for flight stability while 1:12 is more normal. With the dimensions so constrained, the mass can only be increased by using particularly dense materials, and both tungsten and depleted uranium have been used for this purpose.

The destructive power of kinetic energy rounds can be very great and they do offer other advantages. To get an effect at all, a kinetic energy round must impact the target. Consequently, there is no need for proximity fuzes or for the complications of a chemical train necessary for a high-explosive weapon. Complexity in a weapon lowers reliability, and in the case of the more complicated fuzes can be a source of interference by an enemy versed in counter-measure techniques. A major advantage to the weaponeer is that the very high speeds involved result in short times of flight, which is a major factor in accuracy. In all, an attractive weapon option.

RAIL GUNS

A recent addition to the family of kinetic energy weapons has been the rail gun or electromagnetic launcher which, as its name suggests, uses electromagnetic rather than chemical explosive effect to accelerate the projectile. Very high rates of acceleration can be obtained from rail guns, sometimes in excess of 100,000 *g*, and the projectile is accelerated to speeds of many kilometres per second. One demonstration from a rail gun some 5 m long resulted in a 300-g projectile being fired at 4.2 km/sec or, at sea level, Mach 12.7. Higher speeds are possible, and experimentation has already reached the stage where the physical materials of the weapon are proving to be the limiting factor. In the atmosphere, the effects of aerodynamic drag points to the advantage of using a projectile of moderately high mass such as that mentioned above, but if used exo-atmospherically the mass of the projectile could be less, with the advantage of a lighter weapon structure. Damage effects could be maintained by utilising higher velocities, and another recent test proved that a 7-g projectile fired at 7,000 m/sec, over Mach 21, penetrated some 4 in into a cast aluminium target.

THE NEW GENERATION WEAPONS

Progress through the ages has taken two forms: that which has proceeded gradually, an evolutionary progress of many years, sometimes hundreds of years, and that which takes place over much shorter timescales and has a major, almost revolutionary, effect on progress. In the weapons field one of the few step increases in capability can be found, at the early stages, in the appearance of directed energy weapons (DEW). Just as gunpowder and the advent of the nuclear weapon provided step increases in capability, so DEW will offer another rare step increase.

Lasers

The laser is the most widely known of the new DEWs. Discovered in the early 1960s, it has since been used in advertising, films and novels; by the 1970s few decent science fiction works lacked laser weapons. By the 1980s, lasers were firmly entrenched on the battlefield as rangefinders. The more lethal effects possible from lasers were also well known, both the 'soft-kill' effects against sensor systems, and particularly the eye, and the more impressive 'hard-kill' effects where physical damage can be achieved against a variety of military targets.

A laser is a highly defined beam of light which has been intensely amplified. It enables high energy to be transmitted over very large distances in the absence of atmospheric distortion and is why the laser features strongly in proposals for spaced-based systems. The principle and the physics of the laser seems not to restrict its power, this being limited by practical size constraints and the ability to produce the electrical power required. Currently the power recovery is low, typically under 10 per cent, but some work associated with the Strategic Defense Initiative (SDI) programme suggests that much better power conversion is possible; figures as high as 40 per cent have been mentioned.

Because the laser is so highly directional, it must be laid on the target with great accuracy. The slightest miss will result in no effect at all. Furthermore it must be allowed to 'dwell' on the target long enough for sufficient energy transfer to occur to cause damage. Against a small moving target, or from a moving platform, this is a demanding requirement, and the weapon control system which lays the laser weapon may prove to be as much, if not more, of a challenge to the engineer than producing the laser weapon itself. In one respect the task is made easier. The laser travels at the speed of light and aim-off, other than at extreme ranges, is negligible.

The major disadvantage of laser weapons at present is their inability to penetrate weather such as cloud or fog and their tendency to distort or bend as they pass through the atmosphere. Two techniques offer some answer to those problems. One is to use one laser to, in effect, burn a path through cloud and then to pass the weapon beam through the channel so formed. The other, again part of SDI investigations, is to illuminate the target by a scanning laser and from this calculate the degree of refraction being experienced. This allows refraction 'aim-off' to be calculated for the weapon beam.

The effect the laser will have on the target depends on the type and power of the laser and the ability of the target structure and material to absorb the energy. The amount of the laser power absorbed can be quite low, typically under 5 per cent for a wide range of materials. There are also techniques which can be used to minimise laser effects. One would be to make the target surface highly reflective, another would be to ensure that the laser was unable to dwell long enough to transmit sufficient energy. A missile could be made to continually roll, for example, so that the energy was spread evenly. This would be similar to moving the hand under a magnifying glass concentrating the rays of the sun; the burn is only experienced if the hand is kept still.

Microwave Weapons

Microwave weapons would use the same principles which are found in the kitchen microwave oven. The band of the electromagnetic spectrum in which microwaves are found run from the infrared through to that part associated with radio waves. The main effect is to produce heat and that could be the damage mechanism against delicate structures such as aircraft or satellites. It could be particularly effective against electronic equipment. Damage to humans is possible, particularly their most delicate eyes, and there is some evidence to indicate that eye disorders can result from prolonged exposure to microwave radiation.

Microwave radiation can also affect the human in other ways and could induce a variety of symptoms including anxiety, insomnia and fatigue as well as physiological changes in body temperature and heart beat.

Plasma Weapons

A plasma is a gas hot enough to have caused the nuclei and the electrons to separate and results in a mass of electrically charged particles together with the magnetic fields which they generate. Ball lightning is a form of plasma which occurs naturally. This highly ionised gas contains very high levels of energy and can be transmitted at exceedingly high speeds. The technology is still in the experimental stage and is some way from being fielded as a practical weapon system.

Particle Beam Weapons

Particle beam weapons rely on a high-energy stream of atomic particles and the shock waves they form to produce damage effects on the target. The particles are projected at speeds close to that of light (3×10^8 m/sec) and varying systems could use either electrons, protons or neutrons. As with plasmas, a particle beam is a complex structure comprising both the particles themselves and the magnetic field which keeps the beam intact. The reliance on the magnetic field to contain the beam results in some problems in propagation. The earth's magnetic field affects the highly charged beam and can deflect it. The natural repulsion of the charged particles tends to be constrained when travelling through the atmosphere, but in space the beam will tend to naturally diverge. The degree of divergence will depend on the energy of the beam and the speed at which it is transmitted but slower beams could spread over kilometres at ranges approaching 1,000 km.

Considerable research is said to have been conducted into particle beam weapons in the Soviet Union, and since the mid-seventies the technology has been taken more seriously in the United States. Possible application for the weapon system must remain speculative at this stage, but use in space as a satellite or ballistic missile interceptor is a possibility, as is its use on earth to intercept incoming tactical ballistic missiles. The first fielded system might be seen on board ship as a system to intercept sea-skimming anti-ship missiles. The advantage of fielding such systems first at sea is that weight and power requirements can be more easily satisfied and the new generation weapons all tend to be very demanding of electrical power.

Acoustic Weapons

It is unlikely that acoustic weapons would have an application against the aircraft crew because they are by the nature of their environment well protected against noise. There could be an application, however, against ground crews on airfields or against certain structures. The possible effects on other targets can be imagined by comparing the effect on the human being.

The lowest noise which can be heard by the human ear is around 1 decibel (db). At very high levels of noise, starting around 110 db, the body starts to experience a variety of increasingly debilitating effects, ranging at first from apprehension and slight nausea through abdominal discomfort at about 140 db, ruptured ear drums at 160 db, major organ damage at 170 db and the high possibility of death at 180 db. At these very high levels of noise, particularly when associated with low frequencies, parts of the body resonate and suffer ruptures. It is the resonation effect, like that which produces the sound from a drumskin, which could damage certain structures. Aircraft in test have been found to suffer from acoustic damage and designers have to remain conscious of the problems which can arise, particularly near jet effluxes.

Some efforts have been directed in the past to the development of acoustic devices, some in combination with pulsed lights, for use in internal security or riot situations. It is interesting to note that the reason for not fielding such systems is not because they do not work but for quite the reverse reason: they work too well. The effect can be to induce nausea, unconsciousness, and epileptic fits, the latter even in normally healthy people. One infrasound device was banned because of the 'neurological' hazards and some have been worried enough to suggest stricter controls over the use of strobe lights in discotheques.

While these concerns concentrate generally on low-frequency sound, the higher frequencies, or ultrasonic sound, beyond the normal hearing range can also cause adverse effects, including headache, nausea and, over a period, intense fatigue.

SPACE-BASED DEFENCE SYSTEMS

The US initiative to start research into a spaced-based defence system has excited interest in advanced and unusual weapon systems. Much of the adverse comment about the US programme has been made seemingly without knowledge of the steps taken over many years by the Soviets to progress their technology and capability. This is surprising, in that a variety of open sources have given a good background to the Soviet efforts.

Although not space-based, the Soviets have for many years fielded a defence against ballistic missiles around the Moscow area. When modernised and upgraded, there will be a complex of 100 launch sites situated around the city.

GALOSH missiles, nuclear tipped, and designed for exo-atmospheric interception of incoming missiles, will be complemented with high-velocity missiles designed to intercept at lower, endo-atmospheric heights. When complete in the late 1980s, Moscow will have a limited two-tier defence about their capital, with the missile supported by the necessary infrastructure of early warning and target-tracking radar sites. This system in turn will complement the world's only deployed anti-satellite system operational since the early 1970s and tested last in 1982.

Soviet research programmes include most of the weapons systems mentioned before, and the essential surveillance, tracking and fire control radars which go with them. The Soviet Union has had an extensive programme in being on lasers from the time the technology first emerged in the 1960s. Developments of high-energy forms of laser could form the basis of a close-range defence for ships at sea. An airborne laser damage weapon has flown, and testing of a ground-based laser which could be used as an anti-satellite weapon has taken place.

Particle beam and radio frequency research is under way, which could be the basis for a space-based system in the 1990s and research is under way on electromagnetic railguns.

The Soviet Union already has a missile-launch-detector system in space capable of detecting the launch of intercontinental ballistic missiles from the United States and research into improvements in this area is under way. Work continues in the vital field of pointing and tracking accuracy necessary to ensure sufficient concentration of energy from new weapon systems. An accuracy in the order of 1 m in 1,000 km is needed for this purpose.

Space-based weapon systems are likely to be demanding on launch capability. The Soviets have eight launch systems with two more in development, including a heavy lift system. They are also experimenting with a system similar to the US space shuttle. Together with the heavy lift system capable of lifting up to 15 tonnes into low-earth orbit, the Soviets are well placed to continue their current intensive research and development into space-based weapons systems.

6

Attack

Once penetration to the target vicinity has been successfully accomplished, the attack itself must be executed. How this is flown and the constraints under which the crews will have to operate depends on the type of weapon employed and the desired weapon effect on the target. There are five principle profiles used for the delivery of weapons against ground targets.

HIGH-DIVE BOMBING

The high-dive delivery of free-fall or laser-guided bombs offers a number of advantages. Any free-fall weapon is affected directly by gravity. The gravity effect on a bomb depends upon its time of flight and its flight path. Released from an aircraft travelling straight and level, the effect initially is at right angles to the bomb flight path and the bomb soon deflects from that path. As a result, very large sighting allowances have to be made from the velocity vector of the aircraft. As a generalisation, it can be said that the higher the aim-off the greater is the potential error when free-flight projectiles are being considered. This can be seen in practice in skeet shooting, archery or even throwing a stone at a rabbit. Only by keeping the time of flight short can this error be minimised.

The higher the dive, so the more nearly does gravity act along the bomb flight path rather than across it. In the extreme case, the vertical dive, bomb flight path and gravity coincide, and there is no need for a gravity correction to the sighting. Although allowance still has to be made for the effect of the wind on the bomb from release to impact, and this can be quite large if the wind is strong, high-dive attacks are normally quite accurate deliveries.

There are ways of making allowance for wind effect. The first aircraft to attack the target delivers his bombs on a precalculated sight picture known to the other formation members. From the leader's fall of shot the others in the dive correct the precalculated sight picture. The technique is said to have been used successfully by Luftwaffe Stuka pilots during World War II. Certainly the Stuka earned a formidable reputation for accuracy and effect, although the campaigns where that reputation was gained were characterised by good weather; the push into France and the Low Countries, the initial attack of Russia in Operation Barbarossa, in Crete and in the desert. Even for purpose-built and slow aircraft such as the Stuka, it was necessary to have good weather and, particularly, good cloud bases.

Two factors have conspired to reduce the attractiveness of high-dive bombing. The steady increase in the effectiveness and profusion of SAM systems has made the high-level approach, or even the pop-up to dive height, hazardous unless a large investment in electronic warfare equipment or defence suppression has been made. Of greater importance is the effect on the high-dive profile of the move towards the use of high-performance jet aircraft as fighter-bombers.

The Stuka aimed for a dive close to the vertical, dive angles between 60° and 80° being common. Although capable of sustaining 180 kts in straight and level flight, it would enter the dive only a few knots above the stall. Its deliberately large propeller was placed in fine pitch to provide as much disc drag as possible and large air brakes/flaps were extended to the rear of the wing. The dive would be maintained only long enough to lay the sight on the target, to steady the aim and to release the weapon, insufficient time for the speed to build up significantly under the influence of the very high drag. During the pull-out, flown at high *g* with its associated drag, there would be little additional speed increase. The result was that this purpose-built aircraft could enter a steep dive and recover from it from quite low altitude, a few thousand feet.

Modern jet aircraft travelling at or near the vertical have far less drag to call upon. Airframes are designed for high speed, flaps are rarely stressed for high-speed use, although there are trends in that direction, and dive brakes, although fitted, are designed more for the very-high-speed case than the lower speeds which may be encountered in dive bombing. The largest difference between past and present is the advent of the jet engine and the low frontal area and drag of that installation; there is no large propeller to put into fine pitch.

Even throttled back, therefore, a modern fighter-bomber will quickly increase speed in a steep dive. As speed increases, so radius of turn for any given *g* increases as the square and the altitude necessary for the whole manoeuvre quickly becomes excessive. Figure 6.1 illustrates the magnitude of the problem and reference to the chapter on Environment will show how often cloud bases of 10,000 ft exist in north-west Europe. This example shows a simplified dive; if other constraints apply, as was the case in Vietnam, where it was important to maintain speed and energy at the medium levels, the height taken to enter the stabilised dive was greater as was the height used in the dive as the profile was flown faster overall. In this case it was not unusual to enter dives at heights above 15,000 ft, and this was necessary notwithstanding the fact that dive angles were normally more modest than those used by the Stuka.

The advantage derived from high-dive bombing from a weaponeering viewpoint is accuracy and penetration. Penetration is necessary to get maximum effect from a bomb against a variety of targets. The high impact angles also help to prevent ricochet, but it is important to be conscious of the need to keep impact velocities against hard targets within the bomb case limitations if bomb rupture is not to occur at impact.

Under certain weather conditions the high dive assists in target acquisition. When attack direction is restricted to an into-sun direction, the more the sight line looks down the better. Heavy haze is common in north-west Europe at certain times of the year, and under these conditions the high-dive attack tends to look through the haze layer to good effect rather than along it (Fig. 6.2).

There can be certain targets where the high dive may be the only sensible option. Roads and railways traversing defiles could be one, and any interdiction operations against the Khyber Pass would be a case in point; equally, operations

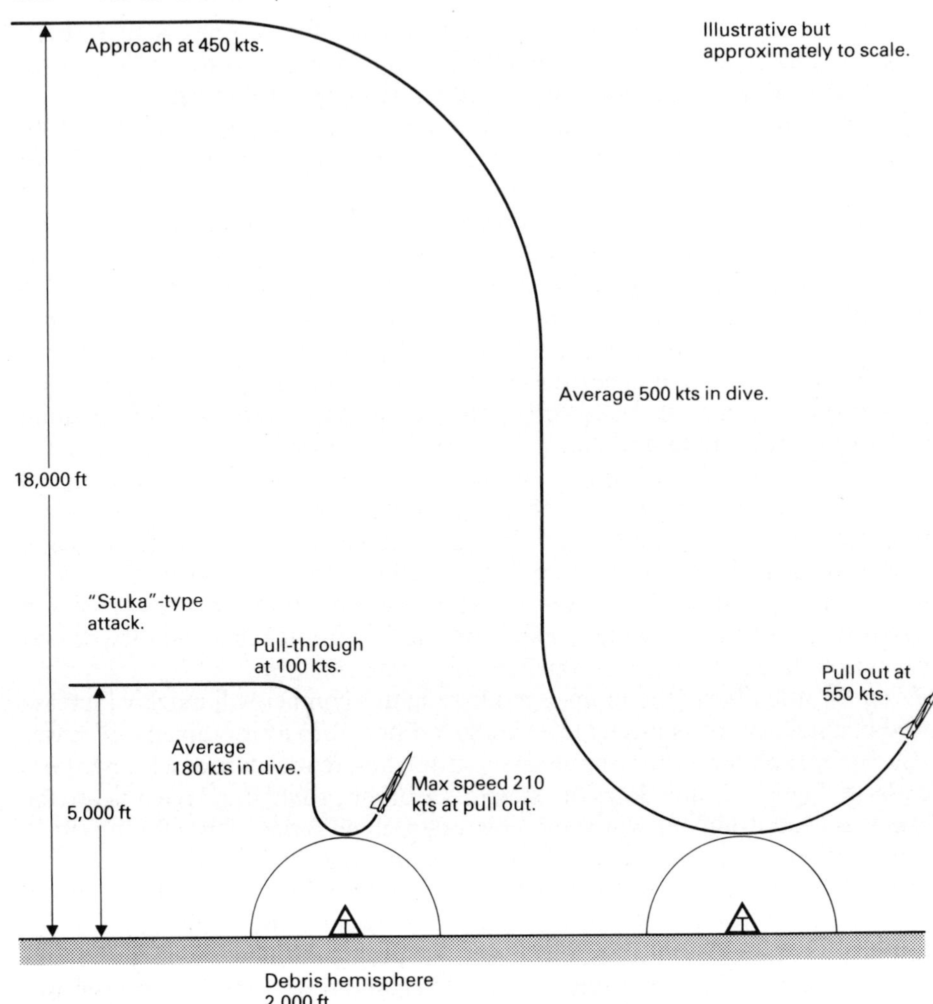

FIG. 6.1. 'Modern high-speed aircraft' attack.

against areas of mountainous terrain, including areas such as the Norwegian fjords or parts of Turkey, both NATO nations on the flanks and both with common land frontiers with the Soviet Union.

While weather, aircraft design and defences have reduced the value of high-dive bombing there are still enough occasions for it to be used profitably for the art to be kept alive, more so as emphasis is given to operations out of the NATO area.

LAYDOWN

As dive bombing became progressively more vulnerable, so a move towards laydown bombing took place. Laydown attack allows the aircraft to stay at low level throughout, and for a long period has allowed defensive systems, particularly those radar-laid, to be avoided. Because the aircraft flies very close to the target,

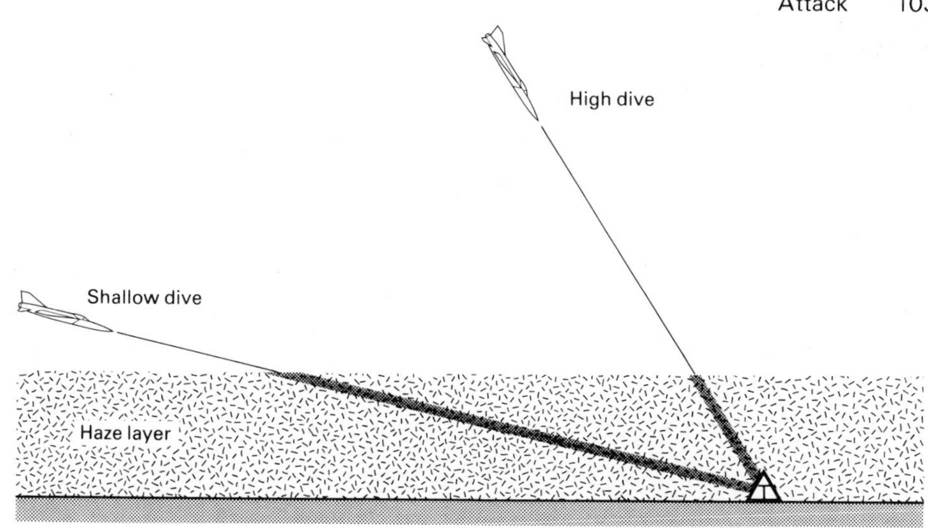

FIG. 6.2. Sighting advantage of using high dive angles in conditions of haze.

popularly at about 150 ft above it, the time of flight of the weapon is short, in the order of only 3 to 4 sec and inaccuracies have little time to build up. Major weapon errors occur in range, and operational stick deliveries allow considerable range errors to be tolerated. An operational pilot using a modern attack system with a stick delivery should not miss a reasonable target very often.

If a ballistic, or free-fall, bomb was released from a laydown attack, it would not fall sufficiently behind the aircraft in the 3 to 4 sec flight time to enable the aircraft to avoid the bomb debris hemisphere. Bombs used for laydown delivery, therefore, have to be artificially retarded. Conventional bomb shapes tend to have high drag tails which degrade the bomb energy with a parachute-like effect; cluster bombs release their individual high-drag submunitions, allowing only the then-inert cluster vehicle to progress along the flight path at a similar speed to the aircraft (Fig. 6.3). The result of the retardation of the bomb is a low-velocity impact resulting in little or no penetration effect. The low angle of impact also encourages ricochet, and this necessitates impact fuzing. There is, therefore, a real weaponeering penalty to pay for the increased aircraft survivability conferred by the laydown attack.

TOSS OR LOFT ATTACKS

Toss or loft attacks became popular as methods of delivering tactical nuclear weapons from fighter-bombers. It not only allowed the delivering aircraft to escape during the time the bomb was in flight, but it was also a means of obtaining an air burst from the nuclear weapon while retaining the ability to approach at low level. Figure 6.4 illustrates the principle.

Because the bomb spends a long time in flight on a toss delivery, typically 25 sec from a low-angle delivery, it can be seriously affected by wind. As it travels from release height up to some thousands of feet before descending to impact at ground

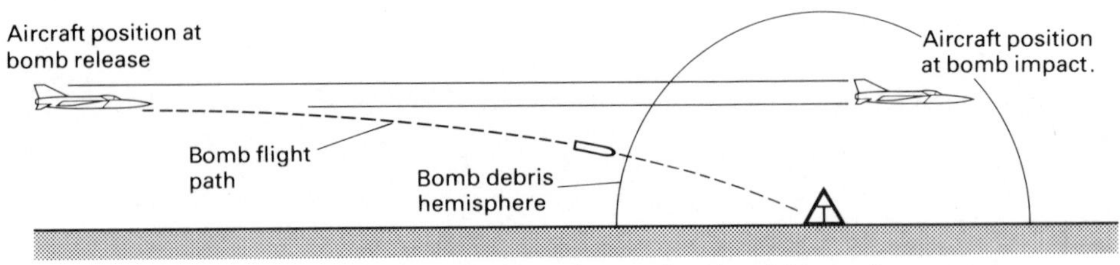

Ballistic delivery at low level – aircraft liable to damage from bomb blast or fragmentation.

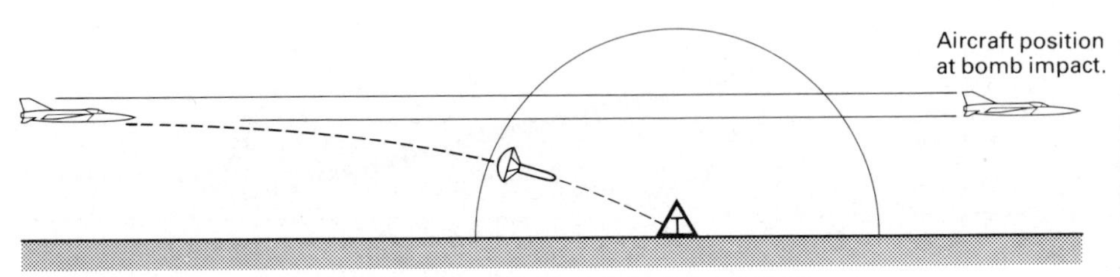

Retard delivery at low level – aircraft remains clear of debris hemisphere.

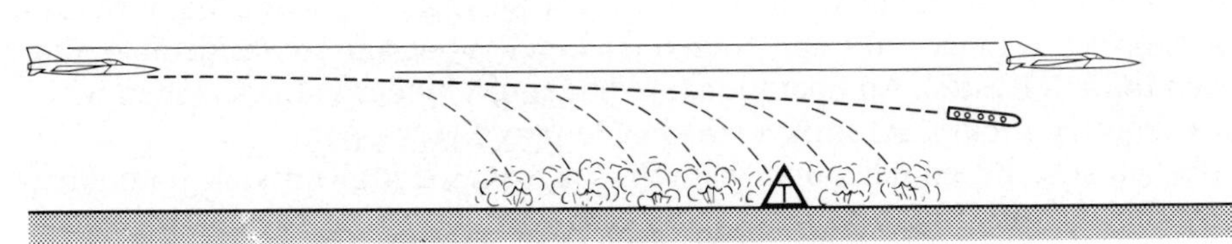

Cluster weapon delivery at low level – the individual sub-munition debris hemisphere is too small to hazard the delivery aircraft. This does not apply to hollow-charge anti-armour sub-munitions.

FIG. 6.3. Low-altitude bomb delivery.

level, it can be affected by a variety of wind velocities difficult to accurately predict and unmeasured or sensed by the inertial system in the delivery aircraft. For this reason alone toss attacks tend to be basically inaccurate, not a major disadvantage where the large area effect of a tactical nuclear weapon is involved, but a serious consideration if conventional bombs are being used. A 30-kt wind would require nearly 1,270 ft aim-off in the case mentioned above.

This would be difficult enough to do in any event, but is more so when the throw distance is considered. Bombs delivered from high speed can fly considerable distances and from a low-level approach it is unlikely that a target will be acquired sufficiently early to allow a sight correction to be made. The aircraft may be pulling up some 4 nm from the target even on a low-angle 30° delivery and at a fairly moderate attack speed of 500 kts. Consequently, the attack is usually flown to pull-up at a predetermined point, or if a convenient geographical feature is not available, on a time and distance from one that is. This is by far the preferred approach, because even if the target is seen, from such distances it is difficult to judge range, although the line of the attack can be profitably corrected.

Toss attack can be a useful option against surface ships. The environment can

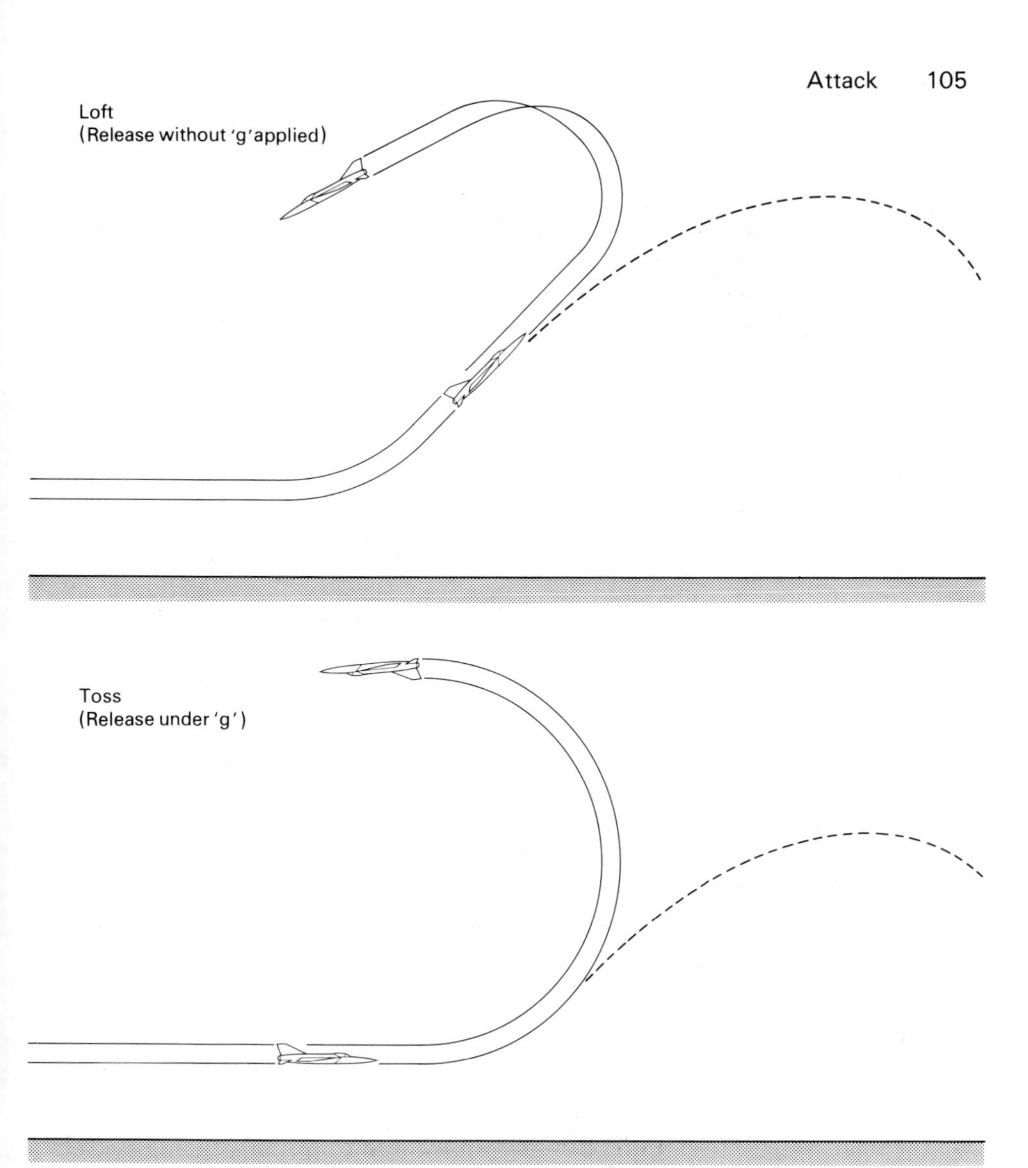

FIG. 6.4. The loft and toss attacks allow aircraft to escape from high-energy bursts or to avoid immediate target defences.

frequently ease the target-acquisition problem—for both hunter and hunted—and the target itself is usually large. Against this there are no convenient geographical points over the sea and it is equally difficult to judge range from a ship. Radar-assisted attacks tend to be the norm, and in this respect aircraft like the Buccaneer can produce impressive sighting solutions. The fact that the ship is moving, and can change its direction if it sees the bombs in flight, makes the problem of obtaining a hit that much more difficult. For this reason, in toss or loft attacks, against land or maritime targets, as large a salvo of bombs as is possible should be used. Although the possibility of a direct hit is low, the effect on a modern warship of an impact of a 1,000 lb could be sufficient to render it non-operational. The probability is low; the return is high—a not unusual weaponeering conundrum.

The weapon which has quite transformed the usefulness of the toss attack is the laser-guided bomb. This is a normal bomb fitted with a strap-on kit which detects the reflected laser energy from a target being illuminated by a laser target-designator, and guides the bomb by means of steerable vanes at the rear to an impact or very near miss. Laser target-designators can be used from the ground by troops in the front line or can be used from the aircraft itself, normally from a laser-designation pod. The Pavespike pod is of the old generation; the Lantirn pod is of a new generation.

A capability which can be exploited with the laser-guided weapon is that as the individual bomb detects reflected energy from the target, the only limit to the number of bombs which can be guided from a single designation seems to be that which results in mutual flight interference *en route* to the target. Numbers of bombs in double figures have been successfully trialled and all impacted on or very close to the target. Very few warships could withstand the simultaneous impact of so many bombs, and the technique lends itself to getting the required amount of high explosive in or about the same place to engage some of the larger and harder interdiction targets. Modern autobahn bridges may require concentrated fire-power to break spans.

The inaccuracy of the toss attack without the use of laser-guided bombs or nuclear warheads at a time when accuracy is so prized almost brings the situation full circle to the time when Admiral Sir Percy Scott, at the end of the last century, was trying to persuade the Lords of the Admiralty to spend more money to improve the gunnery accuracy of Her Majesty's ships. The answer he received was indicative of the importance placed on the subject at the time. 'And what will be the use of more accurate guns?' he was asked, 'The enemy will simply dodge them. With our present pieces they are in danger everywhere.'

SHALLOW-DIVE BOMBING

Although any form of dive attack has met with disfavour since ground defences have become more effective, there is still a need for shallow-dive attacks. The reasons are twofold: the need for target acquisition, about which more later, but which encompasses these days both human and 'system' target acquisition; and the need to deliver some ordnance from a dive profile, mainly rocket projectiles, but including other forward-firing armament such as guns.

There has been an attempt to reduce the required dive angle progressively over the years as defensive systems have become capable of more rapid reaction. Twenty years ago dive angles of 20–30° were common, now much more modest angles are used, and many air forces are thinking about, and a few are trialling, very shallow-angle deliveries of only a degree or so. Some have looked at deliveries of forward-firing weapons from straight and level profiles.

Where shallow-dive attacks are called for, the aircraft has to spend the minimum amount of time possible away from low level. The time taken is determined by the requirements of the weapon system, those requiring long times to lock on or to satisfactorily lay being bad in this respect. The aircraft must first pull-up and acquire the target. The time taken for this will depend on the conspicuity of the target; a bridge should be easy, a tank almost invariably difficult. The aircraft must then be manoeuvred to bring the sighting system to bear and a sight solution arrived at. The time this takes will depend on the geometry of the attack and on the particular demands of the weapons system. The aircraft must then be flown to the point of weapons firing. Some weapons will be very range-tolerant, allowing firing from a wide bracket; a weapon like Maverick, for example. Other weapons will be quite range-critical if accuracy is not to suffer, and guns and the older rocket projectiles are in this category.

Aircraft guns have steadily improved in accuracy over the years, mainly under the influence of seeking better air-to-air performance. Accuracy is closely related to muzzle velocity and the heavier calibre cannon have improved from muzzle velocities of under 2,000 ft/sec 30 years ago to well over 3,000 ft/sec today. This has allowed ranges to be extended from the norm of about 800 m of earlier days to ranges outside 1,000 m today, and for advanced guns such as the GAU-9 in the A-10 to ranges closer to 2,000 m. This, however, is the exception.

Rocket projectiles (R/P) have tended to fade in popularity somewhat after their dynamic development in the early 1940s. The potential of the rocket projectile was recognised first by the Soviets, and British interest was awakened by reports of their successful use by the British Military Mission. By 1945 fighter-bombers were using them to great effect against armour, convoys, shipping and most spectacularly against trains. The 3-in rocket motor of the day, in use until the early sixties, was slow, inaccurate and placed great demands upon the skill of the pilot. Rocketry was much more of an art than a science, and the good weaponeers were those who could make allowances for sighting pictures which were crude by today's standards. The 3-in rocket did have a 60-lb head option, however, and although the probability of a hit was low, the effect once the hit was obtained was impressive. Some aircraft were configured to carry up to twenty-four 3-in R/P and the hitting power of such a salvo was equated to that from the broadside from a cruiser.

Once the motor of a R/P has burned out, the weapon rapidly loses velocity and the trajectory drops quickly away from the sight line. As most operational firing ranges are outside burn-out range, range estimation is of vital importance to rocketeering. While excellent results have traditionally been obtained on academic range exercises, there has always been doubt that such results could be obtained for real in an operational scenario. The high-speed aircraft, unable to generate the small turn radii necessary for debris avoidance, has caused the rocket to be fired further and further out from the target, so compromising accuracy. The slow, heavy 3-in R/P fired at some 250 kts in World War II at ranges as close as 300 m probably proved to be as accurate as the much higher-speed R/P fired from 550-kt aircraft today, where firing ranges are regularly in excess of 1,000 m. Figure 6.5 illustrates the problem in a simplified form.

One reason for the loss of R/P popularity has been the advent of the cluster weapon, of which the British BL755 and the US Rockeye are examples. These weapons release large numbers of submunitions, each with a similar effect to the head of an anti-tank R/P, but can be delivered from a straight and level pass at low level across the top of the target. However, even that is becoming a less attractive option in the face of improved point defences.

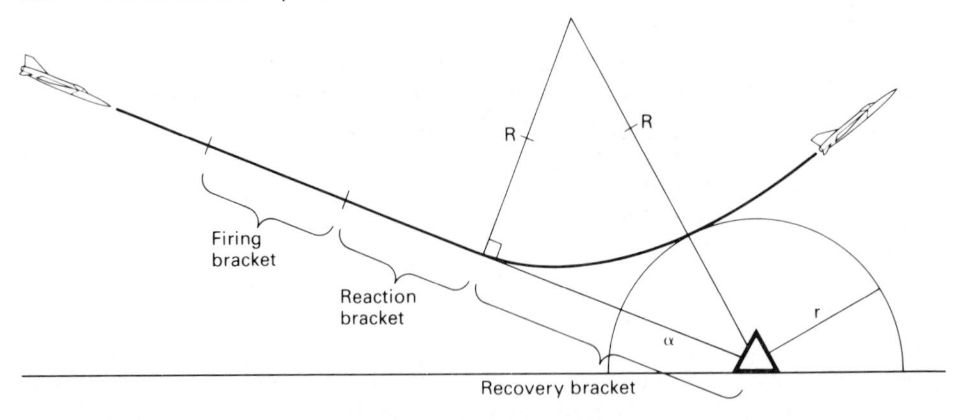

An aircraft conducts a rocket attack against a target at 550 kts and needs to clear a debris hemisphere of 300 ft. If reaction time is 0.5 sec, 6 *g* is applied without delay, and the weapons take 0.6 sec to fire out. What is the minimum open fire range?

$$\text{Range}_{(\text{min})} = \text{Firing bracket} + \text{reaction bracket} + \text{recovery bracket}$$

$$= (550 \times 1.69 \times 0.6) + (550 \times 1.69 \times 0.5) + \left(\sqrt{r^2 + \frac{2v^2 r}{g(n-1)}}\right)$$

$$= 558 + 465 + \sqrt{300^2 + \frac{2(550 \times 1.69)^2 \times 30}{32.174\,(6-1)}}$$

$$= 558 + 465 + 1820$$

$$= 2843 \text{ ft}$$

FIG. 6.5. Calculation of minimum open fire range—aircraft rocket attack.

STAND-OFF ATTACK

The difficulty of acquiring typical battlefield targets early enough to conduct an effective attack, or early enough to lay on smart weapons, combined with the vulnerability of aircraft in the immediate forward area, has lessened the attractiveness of using aircraft in this area. This is not to say that aircraft would not be used; on the contrary, they will be used, particularly in those circumstances where a heavy concentration of fire power is required, such as at times of breakthrough or of counter-attack. However, the option is likely to prove to be progressively more costly.

This situation arises at the same time as technology is offering means of providing submunition warheads with the sensor and data processing needed to search for, locate and attack armour. The Multi-Launch Rocket System (MLRS) purchased for the US Army, British Army and others is due to be equipped with heads utilising such technology. The MLRS has a range of 32 km. A number of nations, conscious of the need to keep manned aircraft out of the forward area if possible, are now looking at this warhead technology to apply it to air-launched weapons which would enable the aircraft to stand-off from the bulk of the enemy field defences.

Opinion differs on the degree of stand-off required and also on the degree of automation. Cost tends to increase incrementally with range; the step from a weapon using only its kinetic energy on release for the fly-out to a bus vehicle using a small sustaining rocket motor is small; the step from this to ranges demanding a small turbojet engine is large. Such bus vehicles become, in effect, cruise missiles.

The problem in stand-off attack, common to ground-based systems as well, is the acquisition of the target before firing. Very-near-real-time target intelligence is required for such systems to be effective, but in this field technology is also offering, for the first time, solutions to the problem.

TARGET ACQUISITION

The factors affecting the ability to acquire targets are legion. Because there are so many, and because so many interrelate and are incapable of useful quantification, there is little that can be done to predict the chance of acquiring targets. This is not to say that a considerable amount of time and effort has not been expended in the attempt to do so; it has, and the effort continues now that the chance of smart weapons acquiring targets is becoming such an important factor in procurement decisions on which rests billions of pounds.

Target size and shape affects acquisition, as does camouflage and its effectiveness against the terrain background. Battlefields are regularly confused with friend and foe intermingled, and one vehicle looks much like another at firing range. The smoke of battle, gun smoke, diesel exhausts or deliberately generated smokescreens can all affect acquisition not only from the human pilot but also from some of the new sensors. The terrain itself may screen targets, particularly where it is mountainous or rolling. Woods are favourite hiding-places for resting armour and for headquarters, as is the close and concealing village or town. Night and weather can conceal perfectly unless aircraft are equipped with modern aids to penetrate both. The technique borrowed from the animal kingdom, stillness, is particularly effective in preventing acquisition. It is the mouse who runs for cover which is seen, not the one who remains still in the corner—it applies to tanks equally.

The tank is the airman's most difficult target. It is small, hard, mobile, camouflaged, and operates on a confused and possibly obscured battlefield. When it is not, it is usually concealed in wood, thicket or in villages and small towns. The head of a pin held at arm's length gives an idea of the angle subtended by a tank, side-on, at the range at which a high-speed aircraft needs to see it if it is to turn onto the attack heading and execute a well-laid weapons attack. A typical Soviet tank is 22 ft long, 11 ft wide and 7 ft high; there is not much to see at ranges of 3 km.

The tank is not the only difficult target to acquire. Even quite large targets can prove difficult unless the attack is planned with acquisition in mind. It might be thought near impossible to fail to acquire an airfield, for example, but this has been done enough times in the past. Airfields differ considerably around the world. In the United Kingdom neatly cut grass, long black-topped runways and high hangars generally present little problem and airfields stand out well from the surrounding countryside with the hangars giving some vertical extent which helps during low-level approaches. Many airfields in Germany are situated amongst heavily wooded areas which can conceal even the hangars. The advent of hardened aircraft shelters has made airfields more difficult to locate, having removed the operating pans with long and distinctive lines of aircraft. The Warsaw Pact habit of covering their HAS with earth blends them into the background better than the NATO system of leaving the HAS uncovered. By its nature an airfield has to be flat itself and situated normally in a flat area; this gives an element of natural cover from an ultra-low-level approach. In other parts of the world, where the terrain is more uniformly light brown than the dark brown and green of Europe, the runway can be the only really distinctive feature, and this has no vertical extent.

When attacking airfields a direction of attack offering the best terrain screening from the defences will be selected if possible. If the defences are screened from seeing the aircraft, the aircraft is equally screened from the defences and from the target itself if they are colocated. This also tends to confuse what ought to be a straightforward target-acquisition task.

The problem facing crews attacking highly dispersed airfields is considerable. Perhaps the best example of this is to be found in the Air Base 90 system in use by the Swedish Air Force where the 'base' is connected to the normal road system and can run for tens of kilometres in an interconnected pattern of strips through surrounding woodland. While vulnerable to ground attack by specialist forces, the target presented from the air and the weapon effort required to neutralise it makes it virtually immune. It is interesting that the Swedish doctrine of dispersal has driven the design of their aircraft, currently the Viggen, while in NATO the reverse is true with the design of the aircraft, with the exception of the RAF Harrier, pinning forces to airfields. An interesting divergence of philosophy.

Bridges are generally easy targets to acquire. A bridge of any size and importance usually carries major communications, road or rail, across some equally major obstacle, river, gorge or other roads or rails. The line features are normally easy to see. Still some unwary attack pilots have been caught out by quite large bridges. Running directly down the line feature which the bridge carries can result in coming to the bridge too late to execute a weapons attack. This can happen if the obstacle being crossed is not prominent or if it is obscured. Large autobahns crossing minor streams, canals or tree-covered railway lines could be a case in point. As it will be rarely wise to bomb along a line feature unless it is particularly wide, approaching bridges at a modest angle, enough to obtain a view of the vertical extent of the structure, repays the trouble taken on planning. Wooded surrounds can present problems of concealment, as can line features which turn acutely immediately before crossing the bridge. There is always a danger inherent in using major line features for lead-in to the attack. If the line feature is carrying military traffic, and that may be the very reason the bridge is being attacked, the mobile units may have integral AAA, either guns or missiles, and its policy may be to engage hostile aircraft with small arms fire. At no time can small arms fire be underestimated.

Because of the difficulty of acquiring targets from the air, and particularly so in the case of battlefield targets, the airman has long sought help from the ground forces. For many years Forward Air Controllers (FAC) have fulfilled the function of 'talking' the aircraft on to the target. The technique is to place a conspicuous object close to the FAC, visible to the aircraft but not to the enemy, and once the crew is in contact with this marker, to talk the crew's eyes from the marker to the target by reference to prominent landmarks. With well-trained crews and well-trained and practised FACs, the technique can be quite effective. During the Radfan campaign in the 1960s some air attacks were called down within a few metres of ground forces. In such low-intensity and low-technology operations there is still a place for the FAC, but on the modern battlefield several factors conspire to make him ineffective.

To 'gather' the aircraft initially and talk the pilot's eyes onto the marker, the FAC needs to see the aircraft. If the FAC can see the aircraft, the enemy can probably see it as well, and that is highly undesirable. The technique is more applicable to the shallow-dive attack, and since laydown attack is more popular the applicability of FAC attacks is less. Good communications are vital and the simple netts used so close to the enemy are vulnerable to jamming, more so from Warsaw Pact forces understanding as they do so clearly the importance of control of the electromagnetic spectrum. The constricting nature of the attack, having to initiate over or very close to the FAC position, does not allow the attack flexibility conferred by modern inertial nav-attack systems to be optimised. The value of a FAC depended on his availability, and the limited numbers which could be trained and kept current combined with the difficulty of moving them about an active battlefield placed further questions on the effort expended in this way. In all, FAC is a technique which has had its day.

At the time the FAC technique was being overtaken by events, the laser found its way into the battlefield, not only as a rangefinder but as a means of marking a target. If the aircraft is equipped with a laser receiver, it can pick up the reflected laser energy from an illuminated target and display the position of the target in the aircraft head-up display. Lasers can be coded and once the appropriate code is set in the aircraft confusion can be avoided and a number of laser-marking devices used simultaneously. Laser target marking has been the biggest breakthrough in the acquisition of battlefield targets during the short history of aerial warfare.

SELF-DAMAGE AND SATURATION

It has been seen that saturation is an advantage the attack crew has to exploit to try to prevent the presentation of targets to the defences in a piecemeal way. It has also been seen that during penetration the mutual support offered by the formation is important in the defence against fighters. The problem arises for the attacker in maintaining both saturation and mutual support during the vital final run-in to the target because of the constraints caused by self-damage avoidance. This is a bad time to be faced by a constraint, because the immediate target area will generally be a most hostile place if the target is valuable enough to warrant its own dedicated defences. Seventy per cent of all US fixed-wing losses in the Vietnam War during the period 1965–74 were experienced within 25 nm of the target area. The situation may become more difficult in the future. Previously the fighter threat could be ignored when entering a SAM defended area; the difficulty of identification and control was too great to mix the two forms of defence. With the advent of the Look-Down-Shoot-Down fighter, engagements can be made from medium level down into a SAM environment operating with a top height limitation.

The difficulty arises in self-damage from our own weapons. A bomb will have its own blast and fragmentation pattern which the delivering aircraft clears by using a retarded delivery. Aircraft ahead of, or level with, that aircraft will also remain clear of the blast and fragmentation. Aircraft coming behind the delivery aircraft will be vulnerable to damage if they pass through the bomb debris hemisphere before time has been allowed for the debris to fall to earth. Unfortunately the debris in this case is not only the fragmentation from the bomb casing but also includes debris from the impact point as well; some of this can be light and can fall to earth much slower than the heavier bomb fragments. It is light only relatively; to an aircraft travelling at 600 kts most things are 'hard'; even a bird can, and has, brought down modern aircraft and bird-strike regularly causes serious damage.

The amount of time allowed for debris to descend must vary with the bomb and with the amount of risk the operating authority is prepared to accept. A time allowance between 20 and 30 sec is common, and risk of self-damage in peacetime operations in a number of air forces is about a 10^{-4} chance of sustaining serious damage, while under operational conditions the risk accepted is 10^{-3}, or one case of serious damage in every 1,000 sorties.

The influence on the geometry of the final attack of the need to leave a 20–30 sec gap between aircraft will vary with the target. A large area target, such as an airfield, may allow for a series of independent aiming points and aircraft can attack simultaneously in a co-ordinated manner, so achieving defence saturation. Against other targets, a bridge of limited size for example, a simultaneous attack may prove to be impossible. If twelve aircraft were tasked against such a target and they had to attack individually, there would be some $4\frac{1}{2}$ min between first and last aircraft over target, the aircraft would present themselves over target individually at about 25-sec intervals, almost perfect separation for the missile units. To obtain this separation, the integrity of the formation would have to be sacrificed many miles away from the target, and nearly as many miles would be required to gather the formation into a viable defensive force for the egress.

One solution is for pairs of aircraft to bomb together. This halves the problem, but at a high risk. If the target is small or needs to be hit with high precision, the wingman will have to fly very close to the leader if his bombs are not to be widely separated in line. If he flies this close, one missile impact or AAA shell strike could take out both aircraft either by the direct strike of the weapon, by sympathetic explosion, or by debris and fragmentation.

Mixes of different weapons and deliveries can be used. If the initial aircraft attacks with, say, BL755 cluster bombs, the debris hemisphere is less and the time delay equally can be less; the following aircraft deliver the weapons with the greater separation requirement. This option is highly target-dependent. There would be little point in using a cluster weapon against a bridge. Another option would be to use a combination of toss and laydown attack. Against airfields this can be an attractive option, with the tossed bombs being a mixture of short and long delay fuzes. Against a point target, the inaccuracy inherent in a toss attack argues against its use (Fig. 6.6).

The alternative often resorted to is to reduce the number of aircraft attacking any one target at any one time. This is a great penalty and fails to exploit saturation.

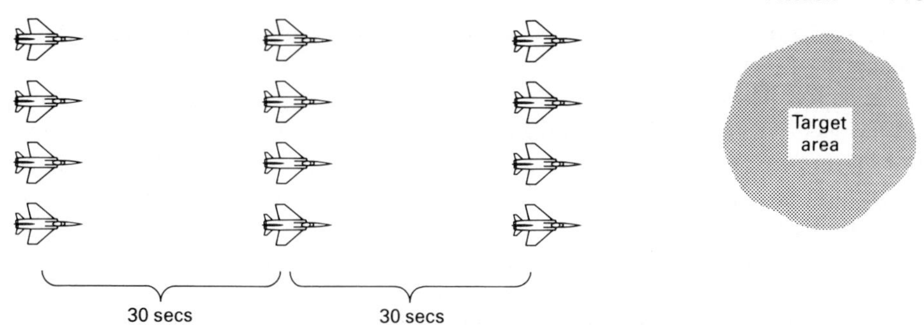

To avoid bomb debris hemisphere and possible self-damage, sections must bomb line abreast and maintain a set time interval between sections. This causes a loss of saturation and makes the mission more vulnerable to defences and to fighters.

By optimising weapon and delivery profiles high saturation can be achieved in addition to maintaining concentration against fighter threats en-route. In this case the first section will deliver a cluster weapon attack, the second will toss-bomb while the third will deliver retard bombs.

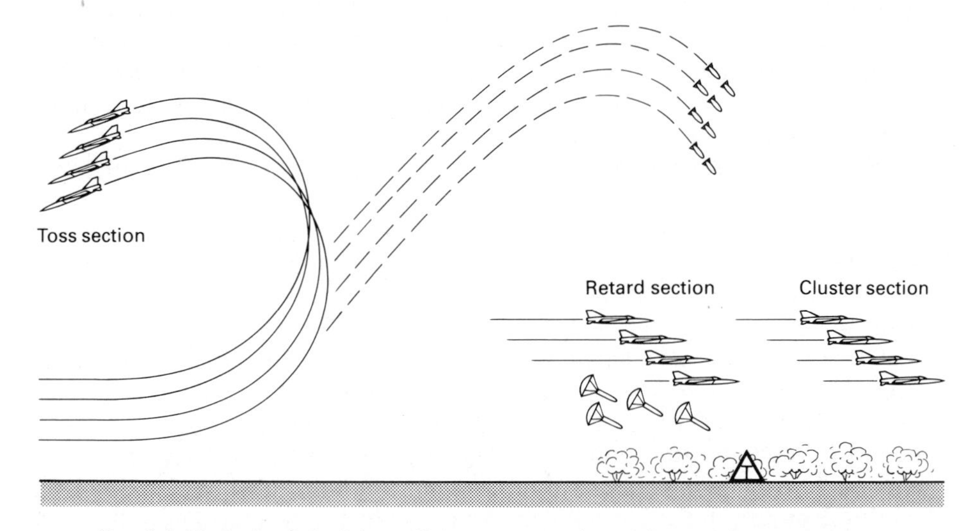

FIG. 6.6. Methods of obtaining self-damage separation while retaining saturation.

A technique offering many advantages is the mass toss attack using laser-guided bombs. Not only is accuracy greatly increased, but the formation can deliver the weapons virtually simultaneously by closing up rather than spreading out as in the case where the need for separation dominates the attack. A further advantage in using a precision system such as the LGB is that the inherent accuracy means that fewer aircraft need to be despatched to any given target in the first place, thereby easing the problem.

The operational planner and the commander must also make a value judgement on the risk that they are prepared to accept. If by separating sections to maintain a one-in-a-thousand chance of self-damage the presentation rate to the defenders so increases their effectiveness that they shoot down one in ten, then clearly the risks must be better balanced.

A major factor working against saturation attacks is target obscuration caused by the bomb smoke and debris thrown up by preceding attacks. This is a real problem and one that can be easily underestimated in peace when most training attacks are made using small training bombs or inert versions of the operational weapon. While the attacks made by leaders may be unobscured and their weapon accuracy unimpaired, the accuracy of following aircraft may be severely degraded if the aiming point cannot be determined.

The wind velocity must be a powerful influence in the planning of the attack. Already it has been seen that the difference in ground speed between an into-wind and a down-wind attack equals twice the wind speed. As this can reduce exposure, it is a tactically sound approach. Even more so when smoke drift is considered, because attacking down-wind means that the bomb smoke is being carried away from the target, along the line of flight, so keeping the aim point unobscured. An attack upwind has the reverse effect, and should be avoided where possible if large numbers of aircraft are attacking from the same direction.

A good stiff wind can be an advantage in keeping the target clear of smoke. This can be more important for attacks from high dives where the lack of a wind will mean that the target is soon obscured. A regular problem in Vietnam, where medium-level approaches and high-dive deliveries were popular, was the identification of a recognisable aiming point. Many crews had to bomb into the smoke and debris cloud hanging over the target (Fig. 6.7). This is one of the variety of reasons why operational weapon results are not as good as those obtained under the far more benign conditions of the academic training range. The difference, known as the 'operational degradation factor', will vary according to target, defences, weapon characteristics, and pilot skill and experience, and can be widely spread. One air force uses operational degradation factors from 2 to 12 in its over-target-requirement calculations.

It is not only the immediate obscuration of the target bomb smoke and debris which can cause the problem. Particularly in the forward area where ground engagements are taking place, targets can be obscured by dust, even in north-western Europe in summer, by smoke generated deliberately or accidentally as from dirty diesel injectors, and from things set on fire as a result of fire from other weapons. This could include anything from burning buildings to woods and crops. Training exercises in the United Kingdom have had to be rearranged in the past because farmers burning straw have caused target complexes to be obscured from the planned approach path. The soldier fights his war largely within a 4,000-m circle and is primarily interested in his normal maximum open fire of 2,000 m. A battlefield obscuration in this order will not materially affect his operations, but will severely hamper the airman relying upon visual acquisition of small battlefield targets.

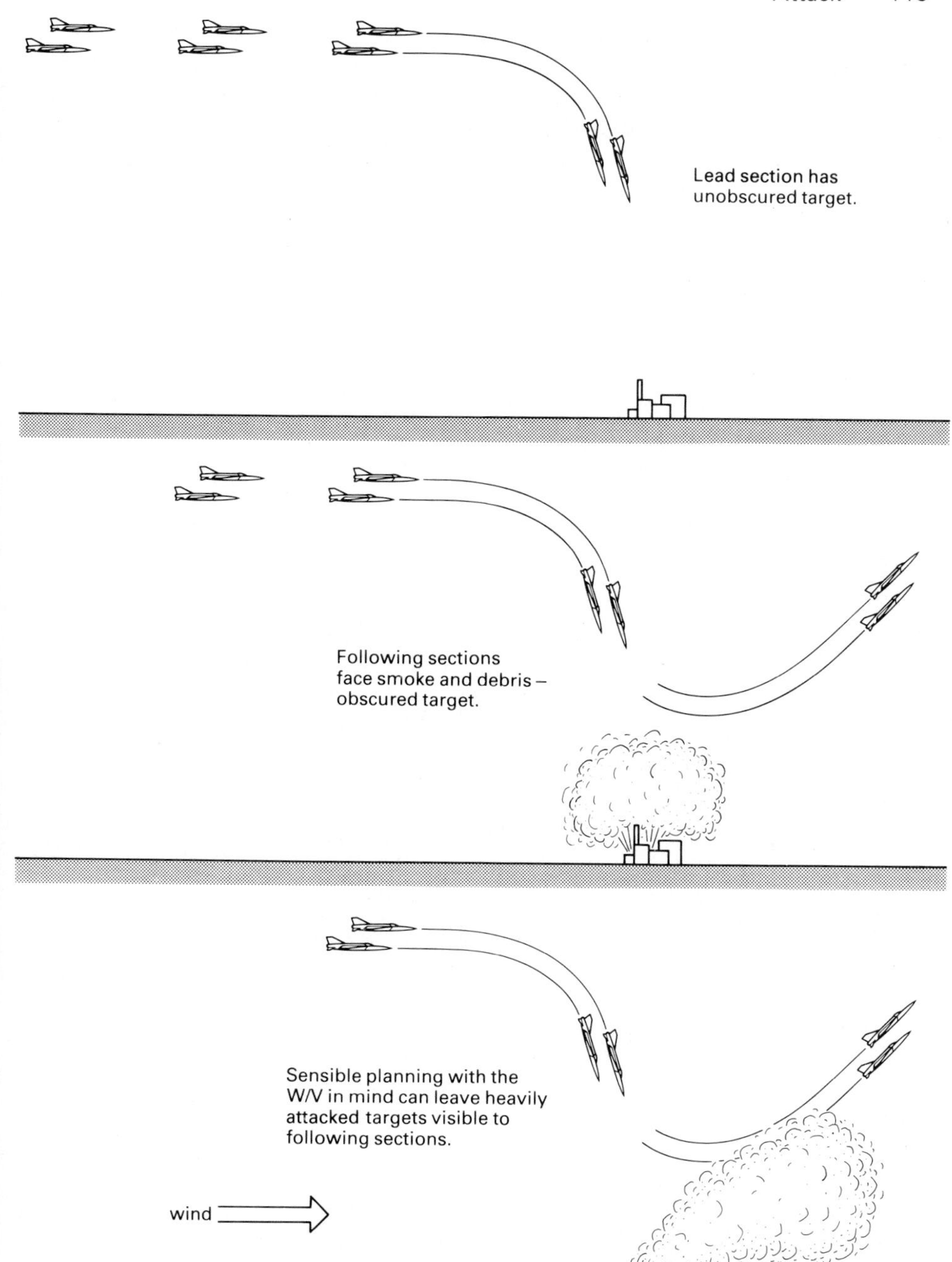

Fig. 6.7. The importance of wind velocity in target-area sighting.

There are some answers to obscuration. If it is predicted, then later aircraft could plan to release weapons on a radar offset, or even on a time and distance from a recognisable point. Against area targets this accuracy may suffice, but would be unlikely to be accurate enough to engage pinpoint targets. Some smart weapons may be unaffected by smoke to any marked degree; most of the electro-optical weapons will be degraded to some extent—some totally—but radar sensors should cope with all but the thickest of clouds. A dense smoke cloud can defeat the laser, and this is yet another reason for attempting to get all laser-guided bombs to impact at the same time, when the laser designator can guarantee an unobscured sighting of the target.

PLATE 5.1. The improvement in firepower which has occurred over the years is shown here with a Jaguar carrying a bomb load similar to that of a B-17 during WWII. The Jaguar is a relatively small aircraft compared to some, with only a 28-ft wingspan. Note the tandem carriage of the bombs, a method which reduces the drag compared with carriage side-by-side. (Crown copyright.)

PLATE 5.2. The bulk of the British 1,000-lb bomb is seen well in this photograph of a loading exercise on a Jaguar. Note the restricted feel and sight resulting from having to wear NBC protective clothing. (RAF.)

PLATE 5.3. As airfields become more vulnerable, so aircraft will increasingly have to deploy off them. Here the author in 1976 lands the first RAF Jaguar on an Autobahn in Germany. The Swedish Air Force regularly fly off road strips and more nations are now starting to realise the value of the extensive European road network. (RAF.)

PLATE 5.4. The laser-guided bomb kit fitted to the British 1,000-lb bomb on a No. 20 Squadron Jaguar. On the outer station is a Phimat Chaf pod and on the centreline a fuel tank. In the rear a Hardened Aircraft Shelter, proof against all but a direct hit by a large weapon. (RAF.)

PLATE 5.5. The large frontal area of the British 1,000-lb bomb is shown clearly here. The shape originated from the internal carriage requirements of the Lancaster. This compares with . . . (Author.)

PLATE 5.6. . . .the finer profile of the US Mk 82 500-lb bomb designed for external carriage on high-speed aircraft. (Author.)

PLATE 6.1. Argentine Air Force Fina A 1A-58 'Pucara' typical of a light attack aircraft which presents no major threat on a sophisticated battlefield but was viewed with some apprehension during the Falklands campaign.

PLATE 6.2. Hawk trainers have to be fitted with weapons for its training role. These confer an operational capability as a fall-out. Here, a Hawk from the Tactical Weapons Unit is fitted with a 30-mm Aden gun pod at centre line, a 68-mm SNEB rocket pod on the right wing and a practice bomb carrier on the left wing. (RAF.)

7

Attrition

Aviation has always suffered from detractors. In the same year that the Wrights first flew, it was confidently predicted by a high-placed source that 'there are no known substances, forms of machinery or forms of force that can be united in a practical manner by which man shall fly long distances through the air' (Simon Newcombe, 1903). In 1957 a UK Government White Paper, presented by Secretary of State for Defence Duncan Sandys, saw the days of the manned aircraft numbered and attempted to swing defence procurement towards missiles. Thirty years later manned aircraft remain on the scene and designs are being brought to fruition to provide manned combat aircraft well into the twenty-first century.

Current debate dwells not so much on the capability of aircraft but on their cost-effectiveness. Cost-effectiveness is, clearly, a ratio between cost and effect, but this can be easily forgotten when funds are limited and many times the term cost-effectiveness is used when 'cheap' would be more correct. A cost-effective system is not necessarily a cheap system. A $100 million aircraft that can penetrate to and successfully attack the target is infinitely more cost-effective than a $30 million aircraft which fails to penetrate, the cheaper aircraft in this case being militarily ineffective.

In making the judgement on cost-effectiveness, the ability of the aircraft to survive is an important factor, yet one of the most difficult to predict. Studies conducted by many nations are legion, and the wide variety of their findings tend to damm them all, unfortunately so because there is a place for considered operational prediction in this area. The reason for the disparity is not the fault of the analyst but of the scenario. Such studies input many factors, each one of which can influence the outcome, some disproportionately so, and the inputs are normally given to the analyst by the tasking authority. Some tasking authorities request such studies to make a point, either way, and by careful arrangement of the assumptions can get a weighty work to support their view. It is a staff technique not restricted to the military world and is to be found in business and industry.

The value of analytical studies of attrition is not so much in the production of an absolute figure—'32.3 per cent of aircraft will be lost on a mission'—for such studies are proved to be poor at that, but in providing an indication of general trends and trade-offs. For example, it may not be possible to say to any accuracy how many aircraft would be lost on a raid, but it may be able to predict that whatever the absolute figure is it will be only half as great if the aircraft are flown at a different height, or at a different speed. The pointers to 'trade-offs' are most valuable to the operator.

One of the difficulties facing the analyst is the accurate assessment of the capability of the enemy. 'Operational analysis' was born in the height of World War II, and as its name suggests was indeed the *analysis of operations.* It had the advantage, therefore, of dealing in fact, events which had happened, and of having reasonable sample sizes. Many of the opposing systems featuring in the analyst's calculations presently have not been seen in use operationally and even where they have, the SA-2, SA-3 or SA-6 for example, they have not been seen in use against particular equipment or tactics. 'Operational analysis' is therefore somewhat ill named for something which is, as much an art as a science—'operational prediction'. The 'art' comes in weighing the importance of certain factors in the absence of hard operational evidence, and it is in this area that scientist and operator must have the closest dialogue.

Very high loss rates are suggested by some attrition studies. One study, frequently quoted in the early-1970s, predicted that if 1,000 aircraft were to be launched against Berlin less than 1 per cent would safely return. Yet real wars continue to confuse the issue with real loss rates considerably less than those theoretically expected. But even then the figures must be treated carefully, for attrition is a minefield for the unwary.

Historically, the average figures emerge to be very low. In low-intensity wars, such as in Korea and in Vietnam, losses were close to 1 in 1,000 combat sorties. For the more intense wars, World War II and some of the conflicts in the Middle East, the loss rate was ten times that, but still only one loss in 100 combat sorties.

These seemingly very acceptable loss rates hide some pitfalls. Although the Vietnam loss rates were only 1 in 1,000 combat sorties, the United States, in operations and training, lost over 4,000 helicopters in South-East Asia. The loss *rate* was very low, but in any calculation the loss itself was very high in fiscal, materiel and human terms. Although the average loss rate suffered by the Israelis in 1973 was only 1 per cent, on the first full day of the war it was approaching 4 per cent. Equally, certain tactics or attacks against particular targets can prove to be prohibitively expensive despite being contained within the total war average figure. The overall 1 per cent attrition suffered by the USAAF in Europe in World War II included the attack on the German ball-bearing industry at Schweinfurt on 14 October 1943 when 291 aircraft were despatched; 60 were lost and 138 of those returning were damaged in varying degrees. This painful experience of a 21 per cent attrition caused the USAAF to suspend daylight bombing of distant targets until long-range fighter escort could be provided by aircraft such as the famous P-51 Mustang, probably the finest fighter to be produced by the Allies over the period of the war.

The lessons shown by history tend to be threefold: first, that overall attrition is approximately 1 per cent per sortie, although averages are more reliable as the sample size, or length of war, increases; second, that attrition can be high initially and taper off once the sortie totals mount; third, the average rate can camouflage instances where the loss rate can be much higher than the norm.

Attrition rates are of great importance to the planner. He may envy his colleague of yesteryear involved in long wars under conditions of high industrial production. When thousands of aircraft are being produced each year, a shortage of aircraft can be met by a temporary suspension or reduction in operations to allow production to catch up with losses. A balance can be struck between production, attrition and operations. Cost does not impose the same constraint when the nation is at war; the ravages of the British overseas investments caused by the two world wars was echoed again during the Falklands campaign where to some extent, even under those relatively benign conditions, money was allowed to look after itself. But in peace, when provisioning for war has to take place, cost is a dominating feature of planning. Further, when the war envisaged is to be short, if for no other reason that it is impossible to make it long, then it is important to get predictions right, or as nearly as this is possible. Too much caution and aircraft will end up without weapons; too little and the weapons will outlast the aircraft. But in this last condition a further disadvantage accrues; the cost of procuring unnecessary weapons at modern costs could have caused fewer aircraft to have been procured in the first place.

Weapon cost is now a major factor in defence forward planning. It has not always been so. It was only in the seventies that weapon cost escalation started to occur to any serious degree, but it now continues inexorably.

The 1,000-lb bomb was designed in the early 1940s and the cost of a current version of it is about £2,000. The BL755 anti-tank cluster weapon, a product of the 1960s, is over five times the cost. The new JP233 counter-air weapon of the 1980s will be mated to the aircraft at a cost approaching £500,000—a salvo of two, which will be a standard load for a Tornado, will cost £1 million. Weapon procurement at these prices must be undertaken carefully and economically, and the predicted attrition rate is a major factor in the calculation.

The difficulty is magnified for those planners trying to procure weapons for multi-role aircraft. Take the F-16, for example, bought by some European nations as a multi-role aircraft in the air-defence and ground-attack roles. When modern ground-attack weapons like Maverick can cost $300,000 and a modern air-to-air missile such as AMRAAM will cost in the order of $250,000, and when the aircraft could be expected to carry four of each in the individual roles, the cost of procuring weapons for a true multi-role capability can soon become prohibitive. To be truly multi-role, any of the sorties the aircraft can be expected to produce during the conflict should be able to be armed appropriately. If any one aircraft is expected to generate thirty sorties in a conflict, then, using the weapon loads already suggested, 120 AMRAAMS and 120 Mavericks should be stocked at a cost approaching $66 million, or over three times the cost of the aircraft itself.

But this would be profligate spending, because in the example being used the aircraft can load only four weapons per sortie, whatever those weapons are. Therefore, during a thirty-sortie conflict 120 weapons of one sort or the other, at a cost between $30 and $36 m would be unused. To avoid this undesirable situation, some judgement needs to be made about the proportion of sorties likely to be flown in each of the roles. This proportion may be 30 per cent or nine sorties flown on air defence, followed by 70 per cent or twenty-one sorties flown on ground attack. The weapon procurement cost for this option would be $34.2 m.

While this approach constrains cost and eliminates waste, it also reduces the multi-role capability. If, for example, the first nine sorties are flown in air defence, as the aircraft is turned round for the tenth sortie, while remaining *capable* of both roles, it becomes *de facto* single-role, because there are only single-role weapons available. So, multi-role capability is far more than the capability of the aircraft and the pilot. It is also dependent upon stock levels which in turn are critically dependent on sortie generation rate assumptions which, in turn, are dependent upon attrition assumptions. The difficulty is that very considerable differences in force level survival and hence sortie generation can result from quite small differences in assumed attrition rate.

If it is assumed that an aircraft on a unit can fly 2.8 sorties/day during a conflict (a figure closely equating to that used by a number of nations), then an attrition rate of 1 per cent will result in the force being reduced to 50 per cent of its aircraft in 24 days of operations. If the attrition is 5 per cent, however, the force is reduced to 50 per cent strength in under 5 days. This effect is shown in Fig. 7.1.

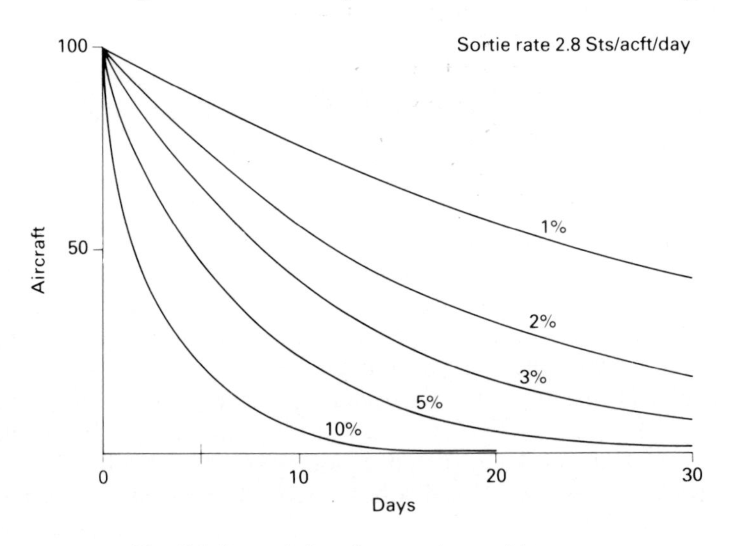

FIG. 7.1. Loss of aircraft at varying attrition rates.

This pattern is instructive to those who argue that attrition will be immaterial, because any war in Europe will be one of high intensity and short duration; time scales as low as 3 days have been mentioned and 10–14 days duration is thought by some to be the limit to certain ground forces' ability to withstand pressure. Therefore, the argument goes that air forces need not worry too much about attrition because the issue will be resolved before it becomes a major effect.

It can be seen that this opinion is misplaced, for it does not require the 21 per cent attrition of the attacks on the ball-bearing industry, or the near 30 per cent attrition suffered on the Ploesti oil-field raids to cause the airman to concern himself about lasting the course. Far more modest attritions of less than 3 per cent can halve his strength before any 10–14 day deadline. Indeed 10 per cent attrition will halve his strength in well under the 3-day assessment used by some pessimists.

At this stage it is necessary to point out that this section is not written to prove the ineffectiveness of air power, rather to show the mathematics of attrition and stock planning, a problem similar to any medium, including ships, tanks and soldiers.

Consider a situation where a force of 100 aircraft are engaged in a campaign. For the sake of illustration consider three force options: the first an aircraft of the

Northrop F-20 type armed with infrared missiles similar to the AIM9L; the second a force similar to the F-15 armed with semi-active radar missiles similar to Skyflash; the third a system like the proposed Advanced Tactical Fighter (ATF) armed with the active radar missile AMRAAM. Putting some approximate values to these packages:

Aircraft	F-20	F-15	ATF
	$15 m	$28 m	$35 m
Missile	IR	Semi-active radar	Active radar
	$50,000	$90,000	$244,000

Assume that on average half of the weapon load is expended on each sortie, and further that a 3 per cent attrition is suffered over a 20-day campaign.

The sorties flown can be calculated from:

$$\text{Sorties available} = (\text{no. of aircraft}) \times \frac{(1 - \exp(-aSN))}{a}$$

where a=attrition rate (0.03),
S=sortie rate per day (2.8),
N=no. of days (20).

N.B. This formula is used primarily in the United States. Attrition is calculated by another form in the United Kingdom and slightly different results are obtained. Over the number involved, the differences are negligible.

From 100 aircraft, 2,712 sorties can be expected over the 20-day period. At two missiles per sortie, on average the cost of the missile stocks becomes:

IR missile	*Semi-active radar*	*Active radar*
$271.2 m	$488.16 m	$1,323.456 m

The large differences in these stock values indicates the inflationary nature of modern weapon development, and it is this, and the mathematics which fall from it, which spurs the debate on whether a lot of simple systems are not better than a few more complex systems. From the figures in the example above it can be seen that the difference in weapon stock costs alone between the most simple and the most complex, a sum exceeding $1 billion, would buy seventy more of the cheaper aircraft.

Examination of the total costs of the three options based on the 3 per cent attrition over a 20-day campaign shows a more marked comparison:

Aircraft	F-20	F-15	ATF
Cost	$15 m	$28 m	$35 m
Cost of force of 100	$1,500 m	$2,800 m	$3,500 m
Cost of weapon stocks	$271.2 m	$488.2 m	$1,323.5 m
Acft plus weapons	$1,771.2 m	$3,288.2 m	$4,823.5 m
As ratio against ATF option	2.7	1.46	1

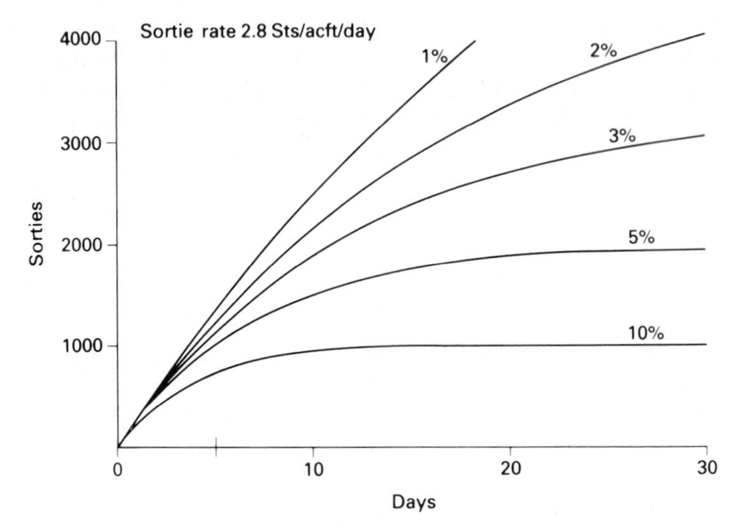

FIG. 7.2. Sortie generation at varying attrition rates.

At face value, this seems to endorse the argument of those who argue for quantity and simplicity, because given the right scenario a 2.7 to 1 disadvantage would be difficult to overcome, even with the more capable equipment available to the more advanced design. The flaw in the argument is, of course, that the more advanced system should never engage on terms of equal advantage. If flown to exploit the performance and its beyond-visual-range weapon system, the advanced aircraft should not be engaged at all by the more simple aircraft while engaging at will itself. It is this factor which returns the calculation to the start; the attrition on the simple system should be greater than that experienced by the more advanced system. But this point also demonstrates the vital importance of the correct tactical doctrine. If this is wrong, neither technology nor mathematics will win the day.

A change of attrition by 1 per cent either way, that is to 4 per cent for the simple system and 2 per cent for the advanced system, means that the sorties produced over 20 days at 4 per cent attrition can be produced by the advanced system in under 11 days. This is no small advantage, as the rate at which sorties can be generated will be important, more so in the campaigns of short duration. Whereas all but ten of the simple aircraft are lost in the campaign, over fifty of the advanced aircraft would survive the same sortie generation.

Another important, and complicating, element of attrition calculations is combat damage. If the aircraft is destroyed, the issue is clear-cut, but if the aircraft returns to base with battle damage this is not normally considered to be a loss, yet if the damage is extensive and the repair time exceeds that available for the campaign as a whole, the aircraft is a *de facto* 'loss'.

In a long war less aircraft will be in this situation because time will be available, and resources will be able to be marshalled, to repair quite major damage and return the aircraft to the front line. A ME-109 in World War II was reported to have landed with over 300 holes in it from 0.303 ammunition, but was repaired to return to battle. Of the 138 bombers returning damaged from the raid on

Schweinfurt in 1943, some 121 were repaired. At that time major cannibalisation was practised and aircraft were virtually rebuilt out of collections of undamaged parts by innovative and ingenious engineers. Then the technology involved was more simple, spare parts were cheaper and more plentiful and manpower was profuse compared with the norms of today. Today airframe damage could prove particularly difficult to repair with advanced structures, complex shapes and modern design spreading load to structure which before would have carried little or none. As speed and *g* loadings have increased, so the need for repairs to replicate the original structural strength has grown; where 'boiler plate' repairs could have been considered before, it is more difficult to contemplate on high-speed designs where aerodynamic shape is so important.

A great difficulty faced by the battle damage repair engineer with current designs is the repair of electrical looms. Even the smallest fragment can damage an electrical loom extensively, and apart from the problem of repairing the wiring itself, there is the effect shorting and dumping resulting from the damage can have on the equipment itself. Modern avionics are highly integrated, with a defect on one possibly causing degradation of performance in others. Just as important is the vulnerability of computer stores and memories to pulses of high power. This is recognised and electromagnetic pulse protection is provided against the effect of nuclear burst, but similar effects can be produced by disruption of the aircraft's own power supplies by fragmentation damage. It is an area where it is difficult, and potentially expensive, to simulate or to test.

Where there is redundancy in a system it may be possible to determine a list of 'acceptable defects'. With aircraft with three or four systems, each backing the other, then the risk in flying with one out is perfectly acceptable. This is common practice in civil aviation, and it should be no cause for alarm. It can be argued that one of the returns for expenditure on redundancy is to utilise it prudently. Military aircraft tend not to have the same degree of redundancy as civil types, however, as redundancy equates to weight and cost and the scope for accepting defects may be limited before the operational capability is affected. Performance deficiencies could be difficult to accept; attack aircraft need maximum performance for heavy-weight take-offs and fighters would not wish to engage in combat with anything less than their full envelope available to them.

There may be more scope for compromise on defects on the avionics side, but the effect on attrition will have to be considered carefully. Operating on the modern battlefield with defective radar-warning equipment, decoy equipment or jamming pods could result in the enemy defensive systems having much increased effect. How many defects can be accepted on the nav/attack systems will depend on the skill and training of the aircrews. Aircrew who are proficient in navigating by traditional map-and-stopwatch techniques may be able to fly a productive sortie despite the modern avionics being unserviceable. Equally, a crew should be able to deliver their weapons with effect despite their full weapon system being degraded or unserviceable. Unless they can, there is little point in launching anyway. But modern sighting systems take a great load off the crew and require a quite different technique than that required for using 'reversionary' methods, many of which are more similar to systems of the fifties, where a large measure of pilot skill and assessment was necessary. As aircraft operating costs have increased, and training budgets have come under increasing pressure, so the time available for this important 'reversionary' training has been reduced. During times of particular financial pressure some air forces have reduced flying to below 10 hr per month, barely enough to keep current on the automated modes.

The effect on attrition of 'acceptable defects' can be many and various. If a terrain-following radar is unserviceable, it may still be possible to fly the aircraft operationally, but at a slightly higher altitude. This would expose the aircraft to more defensive weapon systems and give them greater opportunity to engage, so affecting overall loss rates. A radar-equipped fighter with an unserviceable radar might be able to contribute to the air defence battle by using its infrared missiles and so should not be kept on the ground in an *in extremis* situation. But it may have to be accepted in this case that in not being able to use its own radar missiles it may have to accept the first salvo from the enemy before it can engage at ranges where its infrared missiles will be effective. This could cause a marked increase in attrition, as that first beyond-visual-range salvo could be the dominating event of the entire combat.

Can attrition be controlled? Before a conflict starts, actions can be taken in several areas to lessen the risk to aircraft penetrating hostile airspace. The more advanced the opposition, the more expensive are the counters; electronic warfare pods can cost over £1 million and take up a valuable pylon, so reducing the bombload proportionally. Radar-warning equipment is also expensive, as will be the range of missile-approach warners under active consideration by a number of nations. Decoys, be they scabbed or podded, cost money, weight and drag. The cost of crew training cannot be discounted. Before running costs of fuel, manpower and munitions are calculated, the amortisation of the purchase price of a modern fighter may amount to $10,000 an hour on a modern design. The more the operational doctrine rests upon crew skill and proficiency, the more flying training requires to be increased.

In a long war there may be time to assess attrition, analyse its cause and work towards a solution. There are many examples of this from recent times: gas and the gas-mask, submarines and the depth-charge, radar and chaff. But such systems can take time to develop and can be expensive on scarce resources. In war, money and production resources can usually be made available to meet an extreme situation; what can be missing are those men and women with the original ideas and innovate thought. Such people can be positively disruptive to a bureaucratic organisation in peace, but form the handful of those in war who, like Horatio, hold the bridge. They are, however, in short supply; they cannot do everything.

In short conflicts there will be a severe limit to what can be done materially. As war becomes increasingly electronically biased, then the most that can be reasonably expected is that in a very short time, hours rather than days, the new enemy electronic order of battle can be determined and electronic countermeasure and devices can be reprogrammed to counter changes of frequency, pulse rate, and to identify those techniques which can be used to confuse and deceive. Again there is a cost to pay in massive short-term data collection, analysis, amendment and modification. To achieve relevant timescales, there is a high manpower cost; a difficult case for peacetime establishments to accommodate. Without it, highly expensive equipment could go to war searching for the wrong frequencies and proving ineffective in its counter. Then attrition will be higher than expected.

The only other option is to modify the operational doctrine. This is too often the path forced upon operational commanders and is the one most painful to adopt. Not only can years of training have to be abandoned at the very time it is being called to account, but there is the very real problem of the commander accepting, to himself and to others, that he had misread the situation, that the enemy had outsmarted him. A good commander will accept this quickly and spend his efforts regrouping his thoughts and forces to face the newly emerged threat. The poor commander will persist, Canute-like, in justifying himself and his doctrine despite the facts, to the cost, oft-times the great cost, of his operational formations. A study of Adolf Hitler and his preconceptions before, and disastrously after, the launching of Operation Barbarossa shows an example of this in practice. The theory of 'cognitive dissonance' proposed by Festinger in 1957 goes some way to explain this phenomenon.

No nation is immune from getting it wrong. In December 1939 the RAF launched a Wellington raid on the German fleet at Wilhelmshaven in keeping with its accepted, but untested, doctrine that the bomber will always get through. Of the twenty-four despatched, two aborted, twelve were shot down and ten returned. Such a loss rate persuaded the RAF to abandon daylight bombing and revert to night operations, for which it was singularly ill-equipped. It was nearly 3 years before it had regrouped sufficiently to attack Köln and to present an effective threat to the Reich at night. The salutary lesson of the Schweinfurt raid on the USAAF doctrine has been mentioned. Unescorted massed bomber raids relying on mutual protection were not as invulnerable as was thought, and escorted operations had to be substituted. The Israeli experience in Yom Kippur 1973 showed that since the last conflict defences had advanced faster than the offensive counter-measures. Doctrine had to be highly modified and the defences engaged first before other targets could be attacked. It is not a feature confined to the Western mentality. What heart-searching must be taking place in the Kremlin when their entrenched views on the invincibility of the Red Army have been so painfully found to be at fault at the hands of the Afghan tribesmen. No doubt as painful to them as Wilhelmshaven, Schweinfurt or Yom Kippur—Day One was to others.

During the Falklands 'incident' a correspondent, Brian Hanrahan, trying to circumvent the censorship rules, gave birth to a saying which struck the imagination of the British public. Not allowed to mention combat losses, he reported of one raid: 'I counted them all out, and counted them all back in again.' Hanrahan did no more than every air commander, on both sides, will be doing on that vital first combat sortie in the next war. Until they have, collectively, 'counted them all out and counted them all back in again' they will not know what they face from attrition. They will not know whether their balance of investment has been right or wrong, whether their training was appropriate, whether numbers or technology prove to be the key, whether their analysts and staffs deserve decoration or castigation.

A wise commander thinks the unthinkable, uses the precious time of peace to ponder the unlikely, to work out his options, to do his lateral thinking, because the very basis of his doctrine could be called into question as the survivors of that first sortie land back. He must school himself to realise that if he has it wrong, he will be far from the first to have done so—it was, after all, thought unnecessary to take tents to the Crimea. The good, or lucky, commander will be the one who wins notwithstanding.

8

The Future

Predicting the future is an uncertain task. It has made fools of wise men in the past, and that when technology was moving at a more sedate pace than it is today. A measure of the difficulty of predicting 30 years ahead is to look back the same time. Who would have credited then that man would have walked on the moon and that science was preparing itself to make war in space. Another problem is that the 'future' starts tomorrow and is infinite; providing the prophet waits long enough, all things may come about. A prediction should therefore be limited to that which is possible within a reasonable timescale and falls naturally from trends which are already in being. There are so many areas where advances are being made that some selectivity has to be exercised. One man's choice may be different to that of another.

The very effectiveness of air power and its potential dominance over the battlefield is the cause of the upsurge in defensive systems against the manned aircraft. The investment in this area is massive and the variety of Soviet systems testify to this. The money and manpower tied up in this defensive array represent resources which have been diverted from offensive systems and because of this the very threat of offensive air power has defended against an aggressive foe before any shot has been fired. The reverse is true, and whenever an airman invests in purely defensive systems he must question whether his course is not a measure of the move of the initiative to the enemy. The effect on resources can be great. In World War II the Third Reich had to invest one-third of its optical industry, one-half of its electronic industry, 10,000 guns and almost one million men in the defence against the bomber offensive. Much said since has questioned the effectiveness of the strategic bomber offensive, but the true measure of its effect is to contemplate the level of naval or ground forces which would have had to be fielded to engage a similar level of resource.

Technology is moving against the manned aircraft. Ground-based systems can be larger and heavier than any opposing airborne system. Power supplies present less difficulty and antennae sizes and crews can be larger and work in a less-demanding environment. Developments in radar techniques are increasing the effectiveness of ground-based radars against low-flying aircraft, and antennae on towers, or positioned on mounds, can extend cover appreciably. Perhaps of greater importance in increasing the effectiveness of ground-based systems has been the improvement in command and control systems. What used to have to be provided to a SAM system by its integral early-warning radar can now be provided synthetically from a netted, fuzed and collated command and control system. This can not only increase the effectiveness of the complete SAM system, but can also allow the individual sites to stay electronically silent for longer. This makes the task of the penetrating crew more difficult. Instead of being warned of the presence of SAM by the early-warning radar, they may now first detect the site when the fire-control radar appears on their warning equipment. The time available for them to react is severely reduced and the avoidance of the SAM envelope by diversion from track is effectively negated if the SAM sites radiate only when the aircraft has entered effective cover.

Counter-measure will also become more difficult. Surface-based missiles are not so constrained by weight and size as their airborne cousins. This, together with the move towards greater miniaturisation of electronic components and the increase in the amount of data processing which can be economically packaged, opens up the prospect of at least dual, and eventually more, seeker systems. Already there are moves towards seekers operating in more than one band, and this complicates the decoy or counter-measure task. Making it even more difficult, however, is the amount of data processing which can be done on the received signal. Logic algorithms of increasing complexity can be incorporated as data processing speeds and capacity increase. A decoy or counter-measure must confuse both the seeker and the algorithms behind it if the missile is to be successfully decoyed and that is becoming more difficult to achieve. The trend in data processing and miniaturisation seems to be moving quicker than the trend in decoys and seeker head counter-measures at present.

The disadvantage to any ground-based system is its static nature. Even the mobile systems are mobile only to the extent of a few kilometres per hour. Ground-based systems are not, therefore, a good method of handling the saturation tactics of a well-planned and co-ordinated offensive attack. Until recently fighters were not particularly effective against low-level attack because of the lack of definitive direction and the lack of effective weaponry to use in the ultra-low-level environment. Two developments have started to swing the balance: the Airborne Warning and Control System (AWACS) and the look-down-shoot-down (LDSD) weapon system and missile.

AWACS is the ultimate radar-on-a-pole and has largely closed the gap beneath ground-based radars that has for so long been exploited by the attack aircraft. The attack formations cannot any longer assume that they will not be detected. Defence avoidance is no longer a sound doctrine, because it can be flawed by the presence of AWACS. In future, attack aircraft must expect to have to fight their way into and out of their targets. Tactics against the bulk of the current defensive fighter capability still offers a high chance of success, but the LDSD missile presents a quite different level of problem. A LDSD missile can be fired from a profile which leaves the fighter far removed from the penetrating formation. Consequently, the IR missiles generally carried by offensive aircraft, while effective against fighters which closely engage, are ineffective against fighters conducting beyond visual range (BVR) attacks from a distance. The defence against a BVR LDSD attack is an equivalent BVR shoot-up capability. This is a difficult requirement to reconcile with the demands of a penetrating attack aircraft. The need for a radar capable of detecting and engaging a BVR threat is hardly compatible with a radar needed to ground-map or to terrain-follow. It cannot go without note that even in the *multi-role-combat-aircraft* Tornado the attack and air defence versions have quite different radars and, indeed, quite different fuselages to answer the demands of radar missiles on the air defence variant. If such dual capability is proved to be necessary, and unless quite major advances are to be made in radar technology and processing, the need would seem to point towards larger penetrating aircraft rather than smaller. Yet the trend in the west, with the exception of the B-1B, is in the reverse sense. The 80,000-lb F-111 of the late 1960s was followed by the 40,000-lb Tornado MRCA of the early eighties, followed in turn by, in Europe at least, the 20,000-lb EFA. The 81,000-lb F-15E Strike Eagle could offer a path to the future and a change in the trend, but the political, economic and industrial objections to that design being widely fielded outside the USAF are formidable, despite its clear military attraction.

If it is decided that the LDSD threat has to be engaged and penetrating aircraft have to be equipped with radar systems optimised more for BVR combat than for attack and penetration, a quite different approach will have to be taken to the latter requirements. The opportunities for doing so are opening up. If accurate navigation can be made available without the use of radar and an accurate knowledge of the terrain is possessed, then radar for use in the attack mission can be dispensed with. Developments of the navigational techniques being used now on cruise missiles combined with the three-dimensional navigational accuracy derived from the Global Positioning System should be able to offer a completely passive terrain-following capability. The collection of the accurate terrain data base will prove expensive, and there is still some way to go before a sufficiently comprehensive data base can be carried in an aircraft to enable it to operate flexibly and independently away from a large support base. The trends indicate, however, that this may not be far away.

Operating purely passively will help to reduce vulnerability in as much as the lack of transmissions will prevent the use by the defence of radar-detecting receivers, but as the effectiveness of AWACS and airborne interception radars improve, the advantage of remaining passive will diminish. Regardless, if the purpose of replacing terrain-following and ground-mapping radar is to allow space for a BVR radar and missile system, the aircraft will have to emit to use this equipment. The gain in remaining passive will only be exploited fully when the other observables can be controlled better than is possible at present.

This poses the question of stealth. The subject is still surrounded in secrecy, but certain pointers are available in the technical press. Shaping is important; the avoidance of radar-reflecting corners, particularly revised design of what is now considered the normal air intake, will help as will the use of some of the new composite materials. Ceramics will be used increasingly, and once a radar-absorbent material can be used structurally, and it probably can be already, then considerable reductions in radar reflectivity can be foreseen. In many of these areas the removal of the man from the vehicle with his requirement for cockpit habitability, air conditioning, survival equipment and, a particular asset to detection, a canopy, will greatly ease the designers task.

Radar detection is, however, only one of the means of detection. Infrared detection, possibly from space, or use of different parts of the spectrum, such as the ultraviolet band, or even acoustic detection may all have a part to play in the future.

This is not to argue that it will be impossible for the manned aircraft to operate on a future battlefield. It will become a matter of the cost-effectiveness of doing so. The investment necessary to ensure a reasonable degree of survivability will become progressively greater, and as it does so the balance of advantage may swing towards other systems. In the late 1960s one critic of the US defence budget projected forward and predicted that by the year 2010 the entire defence budget would purchase only one bomber aircraft if cost progression was not better constrained. The pattern of US heavy bomber production seems to support this thesis; there were 2,040 of the six-engined B-47 built, 744 of the eight-engined B-52 and a production run of only 100 of the new B-1 is planned. How many of the new stealth bomber will be built can only be surmised, no figures having been released yet but at least one article in the aviation press has estimated that only 50 could be afforded.

Smaller numbers can be offset by increased effectiveness falling from better accuracies or can be reconciled in the nuclear role where numbers, while still important, can be more modest. If dual capability is the aim, it is more difficult to accept small numbers. If 'dumb' bombs are to be used, as they were from the B-52 in South-East Asia, the weight of attack, and thereby numbers, is an important requirement. Conversely, if smart weapons are to be used which stand-off from the target to protect the large investment in the aircraft, then the clever part of the weapon, its *en route* and terminal guidance, can be placed in weapons which themselves can equally provide the element of the total mission package now provided by the aircraft.

Too much of the debate on delivery systems is clouded by suspect starting points. The purpose of air power is not to exist in its own right; it is to pose a capability to project national will and power. The measure of that, ultimately, is the effect that it can have on a target. Discussion should start at the target and work back to determine the optimum damage mechanism and delivery system. If the weapon is locating and accurately impacting the target, the aircraft merely puts range into the equation.

Range can be provided these days by vehicles other than aircraft. Ballistic missiles have global reach, even submarine-based systems constrained in size can reach 4,000 nm; cruise missiles can have great flexibility of range, and although slower than ballistic missiles can present defensive systems with a different and extremely expensive problem to solve. The Boeing AGM-86B ALCM has a range in excess of 2,000 nm and the new Soviet ALCM AS-15 is credited with operational ranges in excess of 1,800 nm.

Are these systems not equally expensive and far less flexible than manned systems? In terms of cost the balance is much finer than at first appears. The popular misconception is to compare a £1 million cruise missile with an attack by a manned aircraft dropping, say, for example, four 1,000-lb bombs. The cost in terms of weapon expenditure is heavily in favour of the manned aircraft, as the four bombs together would amount to a little under £8,000. When looked at in terms of system acquisition cost, a different picture emerges.

Take as an example a force of 100 Tornado aircraft. It is difficult to obtain an accurate figure for the cost of the Tornado, but a compromise between the figure of

£17 million* given to the House of Commons in an answer in November 1985, the £9 billion UK programme cost for 385 aircraft given as evidence to the Defence Committee† equating to a cost of over £23 million each, but ignoring the estimate presented by an academic‡ of a programme cost of £13.2 billion at FY 84/85 prices equating to a cost of £34 million per aircraft, will give a figure in the order of £20 million.

A force of 100 Tornados would therefore represent a capital investment of £2 billion. The crews to man that force, at a modest ratio of 1:25 to 1 crew-to-aircraft ratio at the training costs of about £3 million for a pilot and about half that for a navigator, equates to a further £562.5 million. If the worth of that force in terms of sorties is to be compared with its value, that is its cost-effectiveness, care must be taken with the scenario selected—the result is, in degree, assumption-dependent. Assuming a loss rate of, say, 5 per cent in the first 7 days of an intense north-western European war, 100 Tornados would produce 1,249 sorties at typical rates of effort. Some 68 aircraft would be lost, but as the argument is being pursued on sunk costs, this will be ignored.

The capital cost per sortie therefore amounts to over £2 million. But other costs have to be considered. In an all-volunteer force most aircrew are on pensionable and well-paid engagements, but they form only the top end of the manpower spectrum which is now a very costly resource. Great strides have been made in the United Kingdom to reduce the expenditure on manpower and the percentage of the RAF budget in this area has reduced from about a half to a little over a third, but the sums involved are still large and in a force which projects itself technologically, manpower is a cost which must be looked upon as a debit item. This is not, of course, the situation where ground forces are concerned. Despite the move towards mechanisation, armies remain necessarily manpower-intensive.

Another cost of the manned aircraft, impossible to avoid, is incurred by the need for regular training by aircrew and groundcrew. The life-cycle costs can be very high, be they calculated on a budgetary 10-year basis or on a 20-year aircraft life. A crew will require 20 hr per month to remain moderately competent on a modern systems aircraft, and even the direct operating costs soon add up to many thousands of pounds an hour, as does the costs of the supporting organisation. This will vary according to the organisation of the air force concerned. A typical USAF base may operate a wing of 72 aircraft with a manpower established of about 5,000. A RAF base may operate about half that number of aircraft and employ about 2,000 men to do so. The 10-year, or 20-year, costs of operating establishments of volunteer, highly-paid engineers and technicians can be substantial; 100 highly trained technicians equate to £1 million per year.

As these costs of procurement, operations, maintenance and support are added together, the 'cost' element of the all-important 'cost-effectiveness' factor starts to dominate the argument. It does so to the detriment of the powerful argument for the manned aircraft, that of flexibility. A manned aircraft can attack an airfield on one sortie, a bridge on another, a tank on the third and sink a ship on the fourth.

*_Hansard_, 21 Nov. 85, Col. 252.

†_3rd Report of HOC Defence Committee 84–85_, Vol. 1, Annex A.

‡Memorandum to HOC Defence Committee by Mr Malcolm Chalmers, Bradford University, HC37-II, p. 338.

While the conduct of a future war defies any confident prediction, this flexibility could prove all-important. How much flexibility can be exploited depends on the investment in training and in the various weapon options needed for the different roles. At this point the argument starts to become circular.

Looking to the future, the manned aircraft finds itself facing an increasing threat from other systems. Increasingly, the weapon will accomplish tasks traditionally the preserve of aircraft and crew. The skills of the crew will gradually be taken over by sensors and data processing. How long the process takes, and it will in any case be decades rather than years, will depend on how well airmen and designers can control costs. Once the cost-effectiveness balance tips beyond a certain acceptable point, it is politician and economist which will decide air power's future course rather than airmen themselves. The declared aim of the USAF to contain the cost of the Advanced Tactical Fighter to $35 million at FY 85/86 prices indicates how well this point has been taken aboard on the other side of the Atlantic.

The general move towards smarter weaponry permitted by the advances in miniaturisation and increased data processing capability means that the manned aircraft will become more the vehicle rather than the weapon system itself. Some airmen rue the day and argue against this trend to their detriment, for it is as inevitable in the light of technological progress as was the triumph of steam over sail or the replacement on the battlefield of the horse by the tank. It is also counterproductive to the airman's cause, for the purpose of the airman must surely be to practice and advocate air power and not be solely concerned with the place in history of the manned aircraft. In the United States there is greater acceptance of the trends than in Europe, and their widely used term 'aerospace' points to the thrust of their thinking.

The airman who defends his young to a fault is also in danger of missing opportunities and the acceptance of vehicle/weapon combinations open up many such options. Some require the acceptance of a different viewpoint on what place the manned aircraft should take, but they are opportunities nonetheless.

Consider the opportunity opened up by the air-launched cruise missile. The ALCM AGM-86B and the Soviet AS-15 are examples in service. More advanced designs are under development in the United States and no doubt in the Soviet Union. The advantage of the cruise missile is that it can remove the need for the manned aircraft to overfly enemy defences. Further, the small cruise missile presents a formidably difficult target for the defences to engage. Being a one-shot device it is vulnerable only *en route* to the target, unlike an aircraft which is vulnerable both on ingress and egress. In this the Ground-Launched Cruise Missile (GLCM) has equal advantage. Where the ALCM is superior to GLCM is that its airborne carrier vehicle can provide an element of dispersal, and thereby invulnerability, but also allows a measure of *envelopment*.

This envelopment, the presentation of the 360° threat, is a most powerful tool for the offensive airman. Of the major tactical cards he has to play, *envelopment* ranks with *saturation* as the offensive trumps. The very threat of 360° attack causes an enemy to regroup his forces and to defend over enlarged circumferences. It is a particularly effective threat to present to a nation such as the Soviet Union, whose great size is in so many areas a major defensive advantage, as both Napoleon and Hitler found to their cost. A major continental power with internal lines of communication and the ability to retreat almost half-way round the globe and still remain in the homeland derives many assets from its sheer bulk. Envelopment is a way of turning size to a disadvantage. Defending the circumference of the Soviet Union against a 360° threat would probably be beyond the resources of even their inflated defence budget. The partial attempt to do so, however, would divert resources from offensive to defensive systems to NATO's advantage.

Is the cost of presenting such a threat prohibitive? Far from it. Consider the earth—for a strategic rather than tactical approach is now being discussed—and consider it for simplicity as a sphere rather than as the oblate spheroid. It is 21,600 nm in circumference, giving a distance from equator to pole of 5,400 nm. Consequently any aircraft, weapon, or combination of the two with a reach of 5,400 nm can, from any one base, cover a true hemisphere. Two bases diametrically opposed can cover the world; from a base at the North Pole such a combination could reach any point in the Northern Hemisphere, and likewise for the Southern Hemisphere from the South Pole. Equally, a force of ALCM carriers dual-based in the United Kingdom and in New Zealand or Australia would have global capability from a 5,400 nm combined vehicle/weapon reach.

Such vehicle/weapon combinations either exist or nearly exist now. The B-52 is an aircraft which can launch from the continental United States to engage targets in Europe and return to the States non-stop. Combined with the 2,000 nm plus AGM-86B, this gives it hemispherical reach. The range can be increased by air-to-air refuelling and it is many years since a B-52 circumnavigated the earth non-stop using this technique. Recently plans were shelved to re-engine the B-52 with four modern technology engines in lieu of the eight older engines now fitted. It was estimated that the re-engining would have resulted in an unrefuelled range of 15,750 nm—or a radius well in excess of 7,000 nm, and that without the reach of the ALCM taken into account.

The Soviet Bear H carries the ALCM AS-15. The Bear is a large aircraft powered by four large turboprop engines. It can cruise at altitudes of about 30,000 ft, at speeds in the Mach 0.8 bracket, and has a range sufficient to make Cuba from the Soviet northerly bases non-stop. Although old in terms of concept and design, the Bear is still in production, and this is quite understandable as its characteristics fit perfectly the requirement for cruise missile carrier. As only the missile has to engage the enemy defences, the relative lack of performance of the aircraft matters little.

The fact that cruise missile carriers do not have to be high-performance aircraft in their own right tends to place some question over two developments, both suggested as having a cruise missile carrier role. One is the US B-1B and the other is the similar approach taken by the Soviets, the larger Blackjack. The performance envelopes of these large and very expensive aircraft suggest that cruise missiles may be only one of their weapon options and that some element of defence penetration is thought to be necessary for the others. Alternatively, it may be necessary because the range of the current cruise missiles are inadequate for the targets envisioned, so requiring a degree of penetration. This thesis is the more difficult to find credible; it is much cheaper to give an ALCM more range than to mount a programme to build a B-1B or a Blackjack. The B-1B programme at FY

81 prices was costed at $20.5 billion for 100 aircraft, surely at over $200 million each, one of the most expensive military aircraft ever fielded.

If penetration is not required, and if the ALCM has sufficient range it is not, then there are a variety of aircraft with the load-carrying capability and range to adapt to the role. Most of these can be found on the aprons of the world's major airports, and consist of the wide-bodied airliners such as the Boeing B-747, the McDonnell Douglas DC-10 and the Lockheed Tristar. They are not scarce; over 600 B-747 have been produced and it is still in production with an improved range B-747–400 as the latest model; over 400 DC-10 have been produced and, as the KC-10, has entered USAF service; and 275 Tristars were produced before the line was discontinued, the RAF having purchased 9 Tristars.

These aircraft regularly demonstrate very long non-stop performance with impressive and commercially viable payloads. An example is the non-stop schedule operated by Cathay Pacific with its Rolls-Royce powered B-747 fleet. The great circle distance from Hong Kong to London is 5,200 nm, but air traffic routing can increase this up to 6,483 nm. The aircraft takes off at a Gross Take-Off Weight of 833,000 lb and can carry 361 passengers and 3 tonnes of freight. Another route flown is Vancouver to Hong Kong direct, a distance of 5,528 nm great circle and one which can involve a flight of 14 hr 10 min if headwinds are encountered. Some time before these trans-Pacific flights commenced a European airline was flying Buenos Aires–Rome direct, a great circle distance of 6,020 nm.

Even without any militarisation of these designs, such as trading commercial cargo space and weight for additional fuel tankage, or ignoring the benefits to be obtained by air-to-air refuelling, these ranges translated into radii and combined with ALCM ranges already give close to hemispherical reach. Of equal importance, however, and arguably more so in some scenarios when allied to air-to-air refuelling, is the long on-station times which can be obtained. The 14 hr 10 min quoted above is for an aircraft flying for range not endurance. Flown for endurance, and visited once a day by a tanker, continuous airborne alert is a realistic possibility. The USAF airborne command post based on the B-747 has remained airborne for over 3 days with no ill effects, and greater endurances are not thought to present any insuperable problem.

Has such a capability any relevance to the United Kingdom? Much depends on the development and interpretation of British foreign policy, for as Clausewitz put it so well, the use of military power is only an extension of foreign policy. But in 1982 Argentina reminded the country that no nation's foreign policy can be determined in isolation from events world-wide, or from the foreign policy of other nations. Perversely, the more industrially advanced a nation, or in Europe's case a group of nations, so the more it needs the stability of market places and supplies for its well-being. Nations with no quarrel can be affected by conflicts far from their shores and by such intangible factors as 'loss of confidence', monetary fluctuations, interrupted supplies of vital raw materials or the swing of markets from civilian to military requirements. The vulnerability of some nations, for example Japan, to Gulf oil is a case in point; the vulnerability of others to interruptions in supplies of scarce metals like chromium and vanadium from the southern African continent is another.

Ideally there must be a match between political intentions and military capability if Clausewitz is to rest easily. The problem for the military planner is that intentions can change far more rapidly than can capability. A military capability can take a decade to develop while an election, or a coup-d'état, can change political intentions overnight. Of all the factors which allow an airman to rapidly redirect his efforts in such circumstances the greatest is *range*, or, more descriptively, *reach*.

The Falklands incident showed this clearly. The 1966 White Paper on Defence reflected the defence review which withdrew British military involvement East of Suez. Part of that White Paper specified that future military equipment would be procured with European theatre requirements to the fore, and that capability out-of-area (OOA) would be accepted as that which fell naturally from the European specification. As a result of 16 years of that policy the RAF front line was being re-equipped with an aircraft, the Tornado, sized to European rather than OOA needs. It was by good fortune that the withdrawal of the once-strategic ranged Vulcan was not yet complete and this aircraft was pressed into service albeit in the long-forgotten medium-level conventional bombing role. An air force well entrenched in a short-range tactical posture aimed at north-west Europe was to transform its operations over a matter of weeks to conduct the longest bombing raid ever during the attack on the runway at Stanley launched from Ascension Island. This was a great circle round trip of 6,782 nm, and that is discounting routing increments.

When the Argentinians launched the invasion on 2 April 1982 the United Kingdom had no means of stopping them during the 35 or so hours the invasion fleet was at sea. Having lost the strategic range of its air power, it had to rely on the only other means of projecting power over such ranges, by sea. Despite having the good fortune of being faced with a situation in one of the few places in the world at such extreme range with almost direct access from the United Kingdom by sea, without the need to circumvent awkward land areas, the 7,000 nm at the average rate of progress of a convoy of about 15 kts still amounted to a delay of some 23 days despite the herculean efforts of the dockyards which enabled the fleet to sail within only 3 days. By the time the fleet arrived at the Falklands the enemy was entrenched and it was only their incompetence and, above all, the lack of in-place air power which enabled victory to be snatched from what should have been a *fait accompli*. The cost was high, variously estimated in money terms in the billions; the human cost was better documented, a thousand British dead and seriously injured.

Is there a better way of handling such a situation in the future? The wide-bodied carrier together with an air-launched cruise missile presents two answers.

The first presupposes that warning can be given of the departure of the invasion fleet. As it was apparently possible to conduct business by telephone with Argentina throughout the course of the 'conflict', it is not beyond the bounds of possibility that this could be achieved within the intelligence budget. As the first ship slips its mooring the warning is received and the ALCM base in the United Kingdom is given 12 hr to react. Within that 12 hr crews are briefed and the 36 cruise missiles are loaded on the first B-747 carrier aircraft. A Tristar tanker is at a similar alert state on another base, both crews having browsed through the contingency plan. It does not take long—it is quite straightforward.

At take-off, the fleet is 180 nm into their 500-nm journey. As the B-747 ALCM carrier passes Ascension, takes on fuel from the Tristar which then descends to Wideawake airfield for its refuel in preparation for the return refuelling, the fleet is 289 nm out of port. When the carrier starts its orbit nearly 1,400 nm south-west of Ascension Island, the fleet has progressed another 42 nm along its route. An hour is spent at the orbit point taking the latest processed target positions from the satellite link and programming the on-board computers which in turn pass this information to the heads of the ALCMs mounted on the external pylons. At the time the first of the salvo is fired the fleet still has 163 nm to go. When the first missiles start to strike, with the same devastating effect that was seen on domestic television screens when HMS *Sheffield* and *Sir Galahad* were hit, the fleet is still 106 nm short of its destination. Fifteen minutes later the second 36-missile salvo starts to arrive from the second aircraft; 15 minutes later 36 more, until the job is done. By the time the crews are back taking a refreshing drink in the Mess in the United Kingdom the Argentinian rescue flotilla has still 250 nm to sail before the search for survivors can begin.

A second, less bloodthirsty, method could be presented by an ALCM capability. It is not strange that the military should be concerned about the bloodthirsty nature of war. A sometimes forgotten fact is that while politicians tend to make war, it is the military who have to fight it. The attraction in achieving the political aim without the necessity to shed blood is clear. There is a deeper reason. If it is considered that, in the Western world, warfare has been judged according to the precepts outlined by St Augustine and St Thomas Aquinas at the time of the Emperor Constantine I, then while the purpose of any just war is victory, there is a strong obligation to seek and establish a just peace. Peace without rancour is far better achieved if the loss of life is minimised. Dirty war often results in dirty peace.

So what if, in a decade's time when cruise missile accuracies have developed to 3 or 4 m, the Prime Minister of the day rings his/her opposite number shortly after the fleet has sailed and enquires whether the opponent has considered that the bulk of his electrical power is generated in the western high Andes and is used in the industrialised and more populous east. And that his predecessor's economy in transmission costs has left him with a limited number of major high-capacity transmission lines running from west to east. Would he like these severed—as a start? How can a nation suitably celebrate the conquest of the Malvinas when all the lights are out? Targetting would not be a major problem. It was a British firm of consulting engineers which planned the Argentinian network. Would a President seeking offshore adventure to divert attention from domestic difficulty—a not uncommon technique used by shaky dictatorships—want the lights to go out? Or the water to stop pumping? Or the sewers to pack up? Conventional warheads at 3-m accuracy open up means and methods of power projection which have never been available before; power projection by scalpel rather than by bludgeon.

There has been much comment about the effectiveness of air power over its relatively short history. Some would have it that the visions of Douhet, Trenchard and Doolittle were misplaced; that air power could not fulfil its promise. Yet the only time it has been given the opportunity to test the theories was in World War II, a mere 26 years after the formation of the first military flying unit. In this case strategic bombing did not come up fully to expectation, but this was possibly more a failure to realise the importance of target system selection combined with the lack of sufficient accuracy to allow the economical use of force than any basic flaw in the doctrine.

It is only now possible to talk of accuracies which will make conventional air power the strategic rapier which its advocates visualised. With accuracies of a few metres, small conventional warheads will suffice against a range of target systems which up to now had to be ignored because of the high force requirements needed, or placed on the list of targets only suitable for nuclear strike. All is now changed, and for the first time air power will have the tools to match its fundamentally sound doctrine.

Another vehicle for which opportunities are opened by the advent of smart weaponry is the helicopter. The helicopter took a long time to gain acceptance by the British services and it was the Malaysian emergency of the 1950s which first proved its worth. Even then the RAF saw better ways of accomplishing their traditional tasks with fixed-wing aircraft than with what was then generally underpowered, short-ranged and low-payload helicopters. As a result, a strange division of responsibility has developed, almost as an accident of history, whereby both the Royal Navy and the Army operate them in offensive combat roles while the RAF helicopter force is currently limited to transport and support roles.

It is probably for this reason that the possibilities opened up by smart air-to-air weapons on cheap simple helicopters for use in the air defence battle have not excited greater interest. Air defence is traditionally the preserve of fixed-wing aircraft, and Tornado F2 and the new EFA will follow that pattern; surface-to-air missiles have also played their part and Bloodhound and Rapier have their place in the order of battle.

Facing the large numbers of attack aircraft ranged against it in Europe, NATO is short of fixed-wing fighters and its SAM belts are vulnerable to pre-emptive attack, saturation attacks and penetration through the subsequent gaps. The fighters that are available will give an excellent account of themselves, the F-4, F-15 and F-16 are very capable aircraft, but there are unfortunately just not enough of them to handle saturation attacks, particularly if they are escorted by fighters.

An examination of the threat shows that there is an element of high-capability aircraft like the Foxbat or Fencer which can operate in all weather and can only be engaged by highly capable defensive systems. It is this part of the threat spectrum where the scarce but capable defensive fighter force needs to be concentrated. But it can hardly be so if it then allows the bulk of the opposing force, consisting of capable even though weather-limited aircraft, to operate unopposed. Most of these aircraft will operate at low level, so limiting the effectiveness of the fixed SAM defences.

The light helicopter equipped with a modern man portable air-to-air missile offers a cheap, quick and highly effective means of engaging this 'low' end of the threat spectrum. The vehicle/smart weapon combination in this case transposes into a *helicopter-fighter*. While the purist may blanche at the term, it is necessary to point out that the helicopter-fighter would not ply its trade wheeling in the classical air combat with a fixed-wing aircraft. It would probably do well in such an engagement, but would first have to locate an opponent willing to sacrifice his third dimension and his speed advantage to engage on such patently unfavourable terms. While this form of combat could be likened to the joust of the knights of old, the helicopter-fighter would operate more like a form of warfare popularised only in the modern age, the guerilla. The helicopter-fighter would attack from ambush; the opponent would run into his net and on to his prickly spines.

Using a missile of the Stinger variety, the average light helicopter could mount between four and eight rounds. Being an IR missile, the system would be entirely passive. The helicopters would operate in a pattern based on a given grid. They would hover in positions which would provide concealment while allowing good all-round view to the extended horizon. Engagement would be following a visual sighting and positive hostile identification. It would be almost impossible for a penetrating aircraft to visually acquire a hull-down helicopter in the hover. The pattern would be two lines with each helicopter 4 nm apart, the rear line half-phase offset. This way there are two lines of continuous missile cover, and it is impossible for a hostile formation to penetrate the line without offering engagement opportunities.

Why not ground base such systems and save the expense of the helicopters? For two reasons: the first because the great advantage of the helicopter option is that regardless of terrain, by hovering to obtain a clear horizon view the problem of terrain screening is overcome. Even on the supposedly flat north German Plain terrain screening is a problem for ground-based defensive systems. Even the odd farmhouse or row of power lines can seriously affect clear fields of view.

The second reason for the helicopter is by far the more important. The technique of saturation used by the offensive formation is effective against ground-based defensive systems which cannot similarly concentrate their fire power. Although fixed-wing fighters can, and do concentrate, a massive raid can find insufficient fighters in the air able to concentrate in time to meet the penetration. Although the helicopter is not a fast vehicle, and the sort of helicopter under consideration here would fly no more than about 130 kts, by knowing the point of penetration the helicopters to either side, by translating towards the track of the raid, can bring missiles to bear. The number of missiles brought to bear is, naturally, scenario-dependent, particularly on the warning time available. However, even a minute's warning, to be expected from a visual sighting from the helicopter screen itself, can substantially increase the possible missile-firing opportunities. If 5 minutes' warning can be given, as may be the case from AWACS, the number of possible missile shots rises quickly to over 100. Bearing in mind that these shots will come from a system almost impossible to detect and difficult if not impossible to counter in such density, it is one which should give the opposition cause for thought, as it must the West if the other side apply the concept first.

It should be a cost-effective system. On face values, a double belt of helicopter-fighters could be fielded, with missile stocks, for the price of four F-15 fighters. The operational concept is so straightforward, and the weapon attack so simple, no more than pointing the helicopter at the target and firing when the in-range 'tone' is heard, that the role lends itself to manning by auxiliary forces.

It is not, nor would it be intended to be, the one single answer to the total threat. For that aircraft like the ATF must be procured at $35 million each. The helicopter-fighter would be a cheap, available, quick supplement to a NATO fighter force which is critically short of assets. It addresses only part of the threat spectrum, but if that part is engaged, the remainder falls within the capability of the more sophisticated fighters.

The third example of where the new vehicle smart weapon relationship may find expression is in the field of defence against cruise missiles. Lest it be thought that in this work on air-to-ground operations too much emphasis is being given to air defence matters, it must be pointed out that one man's vice is another man's virtue. To effectively prosecute air-to-ground operations, air defences have to be penetrated and defensive options are opening up for both sides. By considering a friendly defensive option, pointers can be had to the best method of overcoming enemy defences and so applying friendly offensive air power.

The advent of the Bear H fitted with up to twelve AS-15 cruise missiles has presented the United Kingdom with a 360° cruise missile threat; this is more particularly so as the capability can be reinforced by the submarine-launched, and land-based, versions of the same weapon. The two essential prerequisites of a cruise missile defence is to detect the missile and to engage and destroy it.

Detection will be difficult if only because the size of cruise missiles is very much smaller than conventional aircraft. The radar cross-section (RCS) of a cruise missile may be only 0.1 m^2 compared to a fighter-sized aircraft signature of around 5 m^2. A modern cruise missile design may, by careful shaping, reduce this signature to as low as 0.01 m^2, and some suggest that RCS as low as 0.001 m^2 is possible in the future if the design is optimised for stealth from its inception. The effect of these small signatures on radar detection is clear. Flying low and with range sufficient to effect wide divergence from track for tactical routing, there is little chance of a cruise missile being located by conventional ground-based radar-warning systems. The primary means of detection will be from airborne systems.

Whereas an Airborne Early Warning (AEW) aircraft may detect a large bomber-sized aircraft at ranges in the order of 200 nm, and a fighter-bomber further than 100 nm, cruise missile detection will be substantially less than this. The actual figure will depend on many things: the aspect of the missile to the radar, the quality of the radar system itself, the efficacy of the signal processing, the dimensions of the antennae, etc. Without selecting any AEW system in particular, with target RCS between 0.01 and 0.1 m^2 it would be surprising if workable pick-up ranges in the order of 50 nm did not result.

This poses the problem of positioning of the AEW barriers. As the cruise missile threats are so long-ranged, the preferred technique of intercepting the carrier well out from the target, before release of the missiles, is effectively ruled out by lack of resources. If this cannot be accomplished, and the number and distribution of vital targets to be defended also preclude point-defence, again on grounds of cost, then the most economical compromise is required. This is to be found when the defensive circumference can be reduced to a minimum. In the case of the United Kingdom, and assuming that interception is desired over sea, then this minimum defensive circumference equates to about 1,600 nm.

If an AEW can detect a cruise missile at 50 nm, it can theoretically cover a 100-nm segment of the 1,600 nm circumference, but prudence suggests that an overlap of cover be provided, increasing the number needed to 19 AEW aircraft on-station at any one time, to provide 360° cover against cruise missile attack. AEW aircraft are particularly expensive assets, and because of that in scarce supply. The NATO AEW force is due to consist of only 29 aircraft total: 18 AWACS E-3A and 11 Nimrod AEW3. Providing 19.2 on-station to defend against one threat to one part of NATO is clearly not a realistic possibility.

The problem is worse than that. The number of aircraft required to keep one on-station depends on the serviceability of the force and the amount of time it takes to turn round between sorties and to transit to and from the patrol area. The relationship between total cycle time and on-station time gives the number of aircraft required serviceable and available to keep one on-station. This figure must then be corrected for force serviceability. For example: to keep one aircraft on-station for 4 hr at 1-hr flying range and a 2-hr turn-round, two aircraft would be required on line, as the 4-hr station time and 8-hr cycle time suggests. But if the force has a 70 per cent availability rate, then 2.9 aircraft are required in total. If on-station time can be increased, an improvement in force requirement occurs. If the on-station time in the above example can be increased to 10 hr, then only 1.4 available aircraft are required, or a force available of 2 per station, or 38 to maintain a force of 19 on-station, which at 70 per cent availability equates to a force of 54 aircraft.

The dominant part played by on-station time, and the attractive return in terms of total force size, points to the use of long-endurance vehicles. This conveniently also eases the requirement for large antennaes. A B747-type of vehicle could be considered, but the basic passenger version of this aircraft is $100 million and in the smaller B-707-based AWACS 80 per cent of the total cost is reputed to be not in the vehicle but on the avionics. Clearly large numbers of B747-type AWACS would break the bank.

Airships may, however, provide a more acceptable vehicle for such a role. A modern military airship, larger than those currently flying, could provide up to a 25-tonne lift and hold station for periods of days rather than hours. Allowing a 3-day station time, 3-hr transit out and back and 6-hr turn-round, the requirement falls to 1.2 airships per station. Twenty-three available airships could therefore meet a continuous patrol over a 1,600-nm circumference around the UK coasts which equates to a force of 33 allowing for 70 per cent availability.

Airships may hold an answer to the second major problem, that of engagement and destruction of the cruise missiles. With a detection radius of 50 nm the cruise missile will not be held in contact for long periods, and if the interception is to be undertaken by fighters it is doubtful whether they could react in time from ground alert. On the other hand, the resources required to keep 1,600 nm covered from combat air patrol would be prohibitive. Further, small numbers may not in any case be sufficient, for the offensive doctrine of saturation attack applies as much to cruise missiles as to aircraft, and an attacker would be unwise not to capitalise on its advantages. Heavy defensive salvoes of air-to-air missiles would be required to handle a saturation cruise missile attack. As the detection would be made from the airship and it would have the payload available to carry large numbers of missiles, the opportunity exists to combine detection and interception in one vehicle. After asking colleagues to accept the term 'helicopter-fighter', is it too much to ask them to accept further the term 'airship-fighter'? But that is what it would be.

In this most specialised of roles other advantages accrue to the airship. Even in the small developmental airships airborne today there is space inside the envelope for antennaes two to three times the aperture of that in the E-3A AWACS. By using larger apertures, much better performance against small targets will result. An airship operates virtually free from vibration, the vehicle pulls negligible *g* and the antennae and radar operate in a helium inert gas envelope. If a perfect environment for an airborne radar was specified, it must read something like the inside of an airship envelope.

The lesson of not having AEW in the Falklands was learnt the hard way, and since then the Royal Navy have determinedly progressed this requirement. A form of AEW is now possessed, using a Sea King helicopter as a vehicle. Under the circumstances, this was the best that could be done, particularly as the British carriers at some 22,000 tons lacked the deck capacity to operate the fixed-wing AEW aircraft which the US Navy operate off their 85,000-ton carriers. But the cycle-time-by-station-time formulae is not kind to helicopters, and it is for this reason that the US Navy are now actively pursuing an investigation into the use of large airships to provide AEW cover where carrier air is not available. In the first instance, this is aimed at providing cover for the Iowa class battleship battle groups. It is encouraging that a British airship design is in contention for this evaluation.

These three examples of differing opportunities being opened up, the development of smart weapons, and the change in the balance between the manned vehicle and the unmanned vehicle, are but a few of many possibilities modern technology is now placing on offer. The problems facing forward planners is not a paucity of ideas or options, but a shortage of funds, and this demands that some difficult decisions are made, not least the need to abandon promising areas of research to concentrate funds on those offering greater attraction. It is not an easy task and they deserve some sympathy if only because they will be judged in time by that only perfect science, hindsight.

Those who see science and technology taking man out of the scheme of things dream into a future too far away to affect those alive today. But it is true that man's place will change. If he attempts to hold too close to the past, then technology will overtake him and he will become a drag on its progress. If he finds his natural place alongside, and in partnership with, the exciting developments promised ahead, the result will be a strengthening of both. For whatever technology is, or can do, it is the child of man and man must ensure that he does not end up with an unruly offspring.

Unmanned vehicles will continue to prosper and will eventually predominate on the battlefield. These vehicles will vary from the inter-continental-range ballistic missile, through the tactical ballistic missile and cruise missile down to remotely piloted vehicles and extended-range artillery rockets such as Lance and MLRS. There will be powerful factors driving procurement in this direction, the difficulty and expense of intercepting the ballistic missile, its rapid reaction time, the cost-effectiveness of RPVs, the cost of defence against all-round cruise missile threat. Two particular factors bearing heavily will be the drive towards stealth, ECM and deception, all of which can be applied to small vehicles somewhat better perhaps than on large aircraft; and the savings which can be made in life-cycle costs as unmanned vehicles are made increasingly as created rounds, so saving maintenance and training costs.

The fielding of the new unmanned vehicles and their full exploitation will be governed more by the capability to develop near-real-time reconnaissance covering the whole range of militarily significant targets than by the difficulty of developing the vehicles themselves. The more mobile the targets attacked, the more the reconnaissance and flight-time delays must be reduced if warheads are to be confined to conventional mechanisms. Vehicles with long flight times or slow speed capability will need target-homing sensors and/or in-flight update of target position.

The delays inherent in current command and control systems will need to be reduced markedly to satisfactorily exploit unmanned vehicles. The problems of handling the high data rates of information resulting from new reconnaissance and intelligence systems will need to be solved; modern data processing techniques will have to be employed on a massive scale and much of the assessment and decision-making now undertaken by the human being will have to be done automatically. A commander of the future will have to concern himself before war as much with the capability of his computer program as with the training and proficiency of his forces. The reliance which will have to be placed on computers in the future may need the military to invest more heavily than in the past on software expertise and to change some long-cherished views on staff training and expertise.

Chemical weapon capability will continue to develop, and its implied threat will be sufficient to inhibit operations of an enemy before a shot has been fired because of the debilitating effects of the counter-measures which have to be implemented. The battle between more effective and penetrative agents on the one hand, and improved protective suits on the other, will be waged with a great prize for the victor and almost sure defeat for the side which cannot counter the threat.

If chemical weapons are limited to use against military targets, protection is possible if sufficient resources are expanded. Not only NBC suits are required; aircraft have to be modified and hardened filtered accommodation will have to be provided for servicing and personnel living space. The problems for armies in the field is far worse; the difficulty of providing suitable accommodation for rest and recuperation is that much more difficult.

A far more concerning problem is presented if chemical weapons are used against unprotected targets. In a modern war utilising highly complex equipment, the military is reliant more on support from industry than it has been before, this time not for production as in the two World Wars but for servicing support and repair. Any disruption of these civilian-manned essential services could have a disproportionate effect on the operations of the military. A target which stands out in this way is ports and dock facilities. Much effort is expended in defending the North Atlantic reinforcement routes, but why should an enemy use high-value weapon systems to seek out randomly spaced cargo shipping in the vastness of the oceans, when they have to congregate into ports for unloading? Mines laid in the approach roads and persistent chemical agents on the port areas themselves would cause a great deal of disruption. During World War II the civilian population was issued with gas masks against the threat of gas attack, but the chemical agents available then were far less potent than those available today. To defend against modern agents, far more than just a gas mask is needed.

Weapon development over the ages has gone through relatively few revolutions. Initially, man used his fists and graduated onto clubs, sticks and staves; he perfected thrusting and cutting implements and was imprisoned in this crude 'technology' from the time he first discovered combat until the fourteenth century. The arrival of gunpowder on the scene was the first major step in the development of the weapons war. The second step was the production of far more effective and numerous explosives as the Industrial Revolution gave birth to the early chemical industry and the nitrates became available. The third step came with the fielding of the atomic weapons, bringing with them the nuclear age. Their awesome power and worrying profusion has caught the imagination and there is a tendency to view them as the ultimate weapon. It is too easy, and convenient, to think that the nuclear weapon is the peak achievement in man's inhumanity to fellow man and that nothing more dreadful can be, or needs to be, contemplated.

Unfortunately this is not necessarily the case. Just as the new explosives emerged out of an emerging chemical industry and the atomic bomb resulted from initial research into the structure of matter, so the next weapon systems could emerge from the research now underway on the basic chemistry of life, the DNA molecule. This research is having a marked effect for good and evil despite its early days, and already controversy surrounds it. Some diseases, many of them hereditary by nature, for years incapable of being cured, are now being overcome to the benefit of mankind. Another aspect of the research is the development of life in test-tubes, a far more difficult thing for the average citizen to accept. But will public approbation stop the progress of science? Once a technique has been included in man's inventory of knowledge, how is it erased? The situation posed by research in this emotional subject closely parallels the nuclear case, but neither can be disinvented.

What has this to do with weapons and warfare? If man can make life in test-tubes he can equally make organisms to attack life, but this time far more effectively and dangerously. The spectre of biological warfare has always been there. In the siege of Carolstein in 1422 the Commander Coribut had dead bodies and 2,000 cartloads of manure thrown into the city by catapults to spread disease and pestilence amongst the population. More recently, anthrax has been looked at as a possible biological weapon. The danger and uncontrollability of biological agents so concerned the civilised world that they were banned by international agreement some time ago.

But what happens if suddenly new research finds ways of making biological agents more controllable and even selective in their use? If man has found the secret of the fundamental chemistry of life, something which has eluded him for so long, and as a result can now genetically engineer and unravel the secrets of the chromosome, can he not manufacture for the first time biological agents which act only against those of certain characteristics? Will the future see the ability to produce agents so typed to act only against 'targets' answering a specific specification; to attack the basic reasons for the human being being different; man or woman, black or white, blue- or brown-eyed, or whatever?

It has already been suggested openly in the United States that the Soviets are experimenting in the cloning of agents with cobra venom. Maybe this is scaremongering or pure speculation. Whatever the arguments used to suggest that this is the case, no authoritative source has yet openly denied that such a technique is not possible. Most agree that the breakthrough in DNA research has opened up a Pandora's box of possibilities.

Will mankind be able to rest at peace under the umbrella of international treaty or agreement? The optimist will argue that this will be the case, because it *must* be the case. The pessimist will say that the power offered by the effective and controllable biological weapon would be so great that no leader of a nation who puts the importance of the end before the morality of the means would be unable to resist the temptation. Biological weapons could be an additional trump card in the hand of a superpower, and could prove to be the ace. Of perhaps greater worry is the prospect of biological weapons becoming a way for non-superpower nations to be able to jump the historically short stage of the nuclear age and move to outflank their larger and more developed neighbours by moving directly into the biological age.

It is a depressing thought. But is it any more depressing than the onset of the nuclear age? Or the arrival on the scene of the new explosives in 1800? Or the impact of gunpowder? As man has learned to live with these other threats, he will probably learn to live with biological weapons. The one thing that shines above all others in the study of warfare over the ages is man's enormous capacity for adaptation, innovation and, when he gets it wrong, courageous suffering. How much suffering he will have to endure will probably depend on how well he controls the science and technology which surrounds him. One day he may find the Golden Fleece of a peaceful world—until then there will be wars to be fought and freedoms to be defended—and *air-to-ground operations* to be undertaken.

PLATE 7.1. Battle damage repair under field conditions has never been easy and as the techniques used differ, sometimes markedly, from peacetime standards, much training and practice is required. Another reason for the practice is the inhibiting effect of the Nuclear, Biological and Chemical (NBC) protective equipment which greatly adds to the difficulty. See here the restricted vision caused by the respirator and the difficulty in handling small objects, a rivet, with the thick protective gloves. Thinner gloves can be used but a tear in the presence of a persistent nerve gas could be fatal. (Crown copyright.)

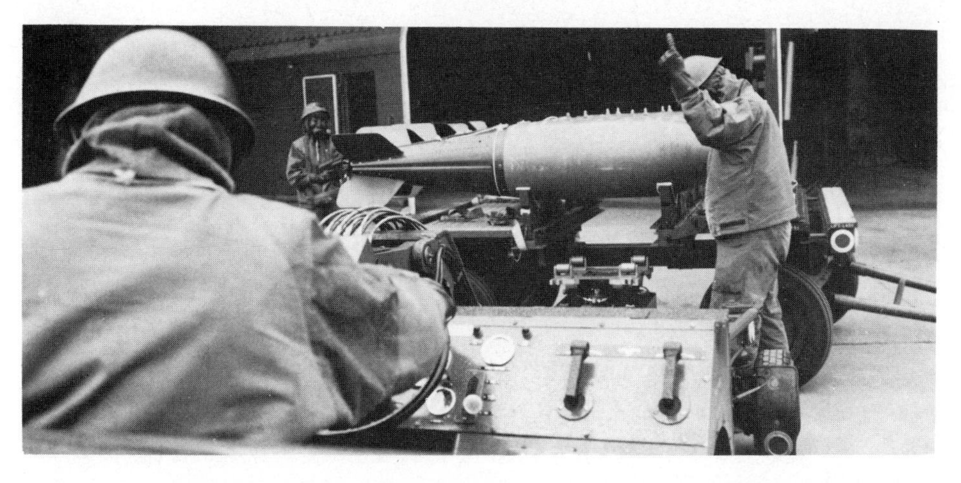

PLATE 7.2. Armourers prepare four 1,000-lb bombs for loading onto a Jaguar protected by its hardened aircraft shelter. The thick NBC gloves can be seen which, despite their adverse effect on touch, will have to be worn to fit the bomb fuzes and the explosive release charges in the pylons. The armourer's task is a strange mixture of heavy humping and delicate engineering with the penalty for mistakes both sudden and catastrophic. (Crown copyright.)

PLATE 7.3. The Sea Harrier, the Royal Navy air defence version of the RAF's close support aircraft, distinguished itself in the 1982 Falkland Island incident. Shown here are Sea Harriers from the three RN Squadrons which fought in that conflict. Noticeable changes from the close support version is the air intercept radar in the nose replacing the laser equipment, and the raised canopy to afford better vision.

PLATE 7.4. The clean sleek lines of a Mach 2 fighter, in this case a F-4 Phantom, are changed by the addition of external weapons and fuel tanks. Such external stores can often halve the published performance of a combat aircraft and this is why combat comparisons need to be conducted with great care. Crediting an opponent with too much performance is almost, but not quite, as bad as crediting him with too little.

PLATE 8.1. The F/A-18, designed as a multi-role fighter and attack aircraft for the US Navy. This aircraft well illustrates current design trends: bubble canopy for improved vision, well designed leading edge extensions, leading edge slats and trailing edge flaps operating in unison, the twin fins for better control at very high angles of attack, and the very short coupling of the tail and main planes made possible by computer control of the relaxed stability. See also the extensive fuel tankage carried externally—seemingly carrier aircraft never have sufficient range for their tasks. (McDonnell Douglas.)

PLATE 8.2. An AIM-9 air-to-air missile fired from a helicopter in trials in the US in the early eighties. This successful series of firings contradicted those who thought the helicopter to be no threat to the fixed-wing aircraft. On the contrary it could prove to be a very serious threat.

PLATE 8.3. The mighty eight-engined B-52, an old design but one still formidable on the battlefield because of its regular update programmes including fitment of the Boeing ALCM seen here. Six ALCM are carried on each of the two wing pylons while further missiles are carried in a rotating launcher in the bomb-bay. The B-52 has an impressive range already, it being possible to fly to Europe and back from its bases in the United States. A recent proposal to replace the eight old technology engines with four larger new technology engines would have given the aircraft an unrefuelled range 15,750 nm; truly a global capability.

PLATE 8.4. The Boeing Air-Launched Cruise Missile (ALCM) (AGM-84) on a test flight. These long-ranged cruise missiles possess impressive ranges, in the order of 2,000 nm, made possible by the small turbojet engines seen here at the rear. This version is equipped with a nuclear warhead, but as terminal accuracies increase the possibility of conventional warheads in the 1990s cannot be ruled out.

PLATE 8.5. The 400 Series Boeing 747. With over 600 produced, the aircraft is in use world-wide. With very-long-range performance, regular schedule services from London to Hong Kong and London to Tokyo are now commonplace. The 400 Series will have an in-service range in excess of 7,000 nm with a commercial payload. Such ranges with the commercial payload replaced by ALCMs would give true hemispherical offensive capability to any nation wishing to exploit it. The missile need not be the limiting factor; the V-1 of WWII was designed originally for air launch.

PLATE 8.6. The Hughes Model 530 typical of the range of light helicopter types which can be used increasingly for military purposes as the trend in miniaturisation and data processing allows highly capable weapons and systems to get smaller and lighter. Such aircraft could present a formidable threat to conventional aircraft at low level if armed with modern self-contained air-to-air missiles such as Stinger or Javelin.

Questions

Environment

1. List the features which together amount to the 'environment'.
2. Outline the visibility pattern throughout Europe, east to west and north to south.
3. Which is the most certain of the environmental features?
4. What is the danger in planning operations on meteorological statistics?
5. What is the order of difference in natural irradiance between a very dark day and a full-moon night?
6. Why is rain so debilitating to an attack aircraft?
7. Why can the amount of snowfall give a misleading impression of the effect on air operations?
8. What is 'white-out'?
9. Wind velocity has two components. What are they and which is the most important to the aviator?
10. How should the air display pilot use the wind velocity to enhance his demonstration and how is the same technique used to advantage operationally?
11. What is 'chill factor'?

Aircraft Design

12. List some of the major breakthroughs in design or materials concerned with airframes.
13. List some of the unconventional wing designs currently under experimentation and explain their advantages.
14. Lift is heavily dependent upon airspeed. How can airspeed be increased locally?
15. List some of the means of increasing structural strength or stiffness.
16. What is a 'bypass' engine?
17. Why does engine development depend so greatly upon improved metal technology?
18. What sort of engine best suits an air-superiority aircraft?
19. What are the compromises in a 'multi-role' engine?
20. Explain the aerodynamic advantages of flying an unstable design and why are computers needed to accomplish it.
21. Outline the system of 'scene-matching'.
22. Give one reason why large data bases will become the norm in aircraft of the future.

Tactics

23. Write on not more than one line definitions for Specific Excess Power, Sustained Turn Rate and Attained Turn Rate.
24. Which of the above tends to be the dominant factor in modern air combat?
25. What kills more pilots in air combat than anything else?
26. Write out the formula for radius of turn and rate of turn.
27. What is a 'dog-house' plot?
28. What technological improvements have resulted in gladiatorial combat?
29. Why is persistence becoming so important?
30. Give one advantage and one disadvantage of reclining seats.
31. Why will helmet-mounted sights become increasingly necessary?
32. What natural features on the ground can be used to enhance camouflage?
33. Explain the optimum method of crossing a ridge line to minimise exposure. (Without using the hands!)
34. Talk for 3 minutes out loud about *offensive saturation* then about *defensive concentration.*

Formation Tactics

35. Who first laid down the basics of formation tactics?
36. How did the Spanish Civil War have an effect on the Battle of Britain?
37. List some advantages of the card formation and say why it is so important for the attack aircraft.
38. What are the disadvantages experienced by aircraft on Combat Air Patrol when waiting to intercept fighter-bombers?
39. Why do low-level interceptions tend to terminate in line-astern situations?
40. Rehearse the technique used to counter a pulse-doppler radar attack.
41. What are the three 'golden rules' for baby fighter pilots?
42. Why was the 'Loose Duce' tactic first introduced?

Tactical Nuclear Operations

43. Why was the first nuclear weapon used against Hiroshima so impressive?
44. Why does the nuclear threat so inhibit Warsaw Pact freedom of action?
45. What is the difference between fission and fusion?
46. What is another term for the 'neutron' bomb and what was its military advantage?
47. What are the five effects from a nuclear burst?
48. How can 'blackout' be used as part of an offensive programme?
49. Sketch out the development of a Mach wave.
50. What are the problems in dealing with flash effects for pilots?
51. Explain the symptoms of radiation exposure.

Weapons

52. What are 'low explosives' and 'high explosives'?
53. Why does an explosive need to be confined for maximum effect?
54. Which travels further: the small light fragment or the large heavy fragment? Why?
55. What is 'spalling'?
56. What is a 'camouflet'?
57. Why do retarded bombs have to be impact fuzed?
58. Outline the workings of a fuel-air explosive weapon.
59. How does a 'hollow-charge' weapon work?
60. What is a 'forged fragment'!
61. What is the limit to the fineness ratio of a kinetic energy rod penetrator?
62. Why are kinetic energy weapons less prone to counter-measure?
63. Give two examples of directed energy weapons.

Attack

64. Why was the Stuka such an excellent dive bomber?
65. Why is steep-dive bombing inherently the most accurate form of bombing?
66. What operational factor caused the move towards laydown bombing?
67. What are the advantages and disadvantages of toss bombing?
68. How can toss bombing inaccuracies be taken out by technology?
69. Why has the rocket projectile lapsed into temporary unpopularity?
70. List some factors which hinder target acquisition on the battlefield.
71. How large is the average Soviet tank?
72. What do you think of the efficiency of the Forward Air Controller on the European Battlefield?
73. Outline the factors affecting self-damage risk and mention the levels considered prudent in war and peace.
74. Write down some of the considerations concerning a co-ordinated mass attack against a point-defended target.
75. How can the problem of target obscuration be eased?

Attrition

76. From the study of the formula for attrition, where, as a commander, would you put your effort in an attempt to optimise your war capability?
77. As a Minister of Defence, would you be impressed by the many/cheap or the few/expensive argument? Why?
78. How can the relationship between battle damage rates and the length of the war badly affect well-laid plans?
79. What was an 'acceptable' attrition rate in World War II? Will it be acceptable in the next war? What are the factors which will have changed?

The Future

80. What are the pros and cons of airships?
81. What reach is needed to obtain true hemispherical capability? How did you derive this?
82. What ranges are possible from the latest cruise missiles?
83. What is 'envelopment' and how does it hurt the continental power?
84. Why does the lack of aircraft performance not affect the helicopter's ability to be an effective air-to-air fighter?
85. The envelope of an air-to-air missile used from a helicopter has a characteristic shape. What is it?
86. Why has the current research into the DNA molecule such importance to the military situation?
87. Consider the mathematics involved in protecting the United Kingdom from all-round attack by cruise missiles and apply this to the number of AEW aircraft programmed to be procured. Conclude!

About the Author

THERE can be few officers serving with the Royal Air Force today who have had wider experience of all aspects of fighter tactics and development—Air Defence, Ground Attack and Fighter Reconnaissance—than Air Vice Marshal John Walker.

In addition to service with fighter squadrons in the United Kingdom, with RAF Germany, and on exchange with the United States Air Force, he has had responsibility for the tactical development of ground attack weapons and systems with the Air Development Squadron of the Central Fighter Establishment, commanded the Offensive Support Cell of the Central Tactics and Trials Organisation and formed the Jaguar Conversion Team. For his work as commander of the Jaguar Operational Conversion Unit at Lossiemouth he was awarded the Air Force Cross. Then followed Station Command of RAF Lossiemouth and RAF Bruggen in Germany—for which he was appointed CBE. After serving as Group Captain Offensive Operations at Headquarters RAF Germany, he attended the Royal College of Defence Studies before becoming Director of Forward Plans RAF in the Ministry of Defence. He is now Senior Air Staff Officer RAF Strike Command and Deputy Chief of Staff (Operations and Intelligence) United Kingdom Air Forces.

Index